PRACTICAL CHROMATOGRAPHIC TECHNIQUES

Newnes Practical Science Books

A series of practical books providing up-to-date information on modern experimental techniques. The books are written by well-known authorities.

PRACTICAL CHROMATOGRAPHIC TECHNIQUES
by A. H. Gordon, B.A., Ph.D. (*National Institute for Medical Research*) and J. E. Eastoe, B.Sc., Ph.D., A.R.C.S., D.I.C., (*Department of Dental Science, Royal College of Surgeons of England*)

GAS CHROMATOGRAPHY
by D. Ambrose, Ph.D., F.R.I.C. (*National Chemical Laboratory, D.S.I.R.*) and Barbara A. Ambrose, B.Sc.

OPTICAL MICROSCOPE TECHNIQUE
by D. Birchon, B.Sc., A.I.M., A.I.Mar.E., F.R.M.S. (*Admiralty Materials Laboratory*)

RADIOISOTOPE LABORATORY TECHNIQUES
by R. A. Faires and B. H. Parks (*Isotope School U.K.A.E.A., Wantage*)

ZONE REFINING AND ALLIED TECHNIQUES
by N. L. Parr, M.I.Mech.E., F.I.M. (*Admiralty Materials Laboratory*)

LABORATORY DISTILLATION PRACTICE
by E. A. Coulson, M.A., D.Sc., and E. F. G. Herington, D.Sc., A.R.C.S. (*National Chemical Laboratory, D.S.I.R.*)

LABORATORY GLASSBLOWING
by L. M. Parr in collaboration with C. A. Hendley

LOW-TEMPERATURE TECHNIQUES
by F. Din, A.R.C.S., B.Sc., Ph.D., and A. H. Cockett, B.Sc., F.Inst.P. (*British Oxygen Research and Development Ltd.*)

RADIATION COUNTERS AND DETECTORS
by C. C. H. Washtell (*Labgear Ltd.*)

GLASS FIBRE REINFORCED PLASTICS
Edited by A. de Dani

AN INTRODUCTION TO VACUUM TECHNIQUE
A. H. Turnbull, B.Sc., R. S. Barton and J. C. Rivière, M.Sc., Ph.D. (*U.K.A.E.A.*)

Other titles in preparation

PRACTICAL CHROMATOGRAPHIC TECHNIQUES

by

A. H. GORDON, B.A., Ph.D.
National Institute for Medical Research, London

and

J. E. EASTOE, B.Sc., Ph.D., A.R.C.S., D.I.C.
Department of Dental Science, Royal College of Surgeons of England

LONDON
GEORGE NEWNES LIMITED
TOWER HOUSE, SOUTHAMPTON STREET,
LONDON, W.C.2

First Published 1964

Printed in Great Britain by
Butler & Tanner Ltd., Frome and London

PREFACE

Chromatography in one or another of its various forms has been successfully used for separating mixtures of so many different types of substances that in all probability it is now used more frequently for both qualitative and quantitative analysis and for preparative purposes than any other comparable method. While the use of all kinds of chromatogram has increased very greatly during the last 20 years, the growth of partition chromatography, which was introduced by A. J. P. Martin, and R. L. M. Synge in 1941, has been the most rapid. The present very wide employment of this method in many chemical and in the great majority of biochemical laboratories is sufficient indication of the importance of the advance which was made by Martin and Synge. One of the present authors (A. H. G.) was fortunate enough to be introduced to chromatography in 1941 by Dr. Synge. The first partition chromatograms were columns of silica gel coloured yellow by methyl orange. These were employed to separate mixtures of acetyl amino acids. The pink bands which moved rapidly downwards were a memorable sight.

While the early results obtained with partition chromatography suggested something of the potentialities of the method, the rapidity of its spread into many different fields certainly could not have been foreseen. Probably the main reasons why paper chromatography was quickly accepted as a useful laboratory method were its great simplicity and the very considerable amounts of information which can thus be obtained. Most other types of chromatogram require rather more attention but none of the manipulations is difficult to carry out. However, to obtain optimum results, care must be taken with certain crucial steps in the procedure, as well as in the design of apparatus. The primary function of this book, which is directed towards the interests of the beginner, is to describe established chromatographic techniques, with an emphasis on those practical points which are essential for good results. The early chapters introduce the nature of chromatography, its mechanisms, the essentials of its quantitative theory and a critical description of apparatus, without assuming any previous knowledge on the part of the reader.

Full exploitation of the chromatographic process, however, calls for more than a careful application of established methods. The separation of mixtures of unknown substances requires the use of an adequate adsorbent and solvent or solvent mixture, the selection of all of which may present difficulty. Success, in these circumstances, must depend both on knowledge of what has already been achieved with mixtures of similar substances and on those general principles which have been deduced from past experience. We have therefore attempted to lay emphasis, throughout the book, on a practical evaluation of the various materials suitable for the stationary phase of chromatograms, and on the selection of solvents in relation to both the properties of the substances being separated and to the probable mechanisms operating. The final chapter contains a description of thin-layer chromatography and specially developed chromatographic materials, including modified celluloses and dextrans. If this book succeeds in helping the reader to build up a working knowledge of chromatography, it will have served its purpose.

A. H. G.

J. E. E.

CONTENTS

ACKNOWLEDGEMENTS

The authors are grateful to a number of individuals and organizations for permission to reproduce in this book illustrations from their publications. In particular, thanks are due to Professor C. E. Dent, F.R.S., for Fig. 3.19, Dr. A. A. Leach for Fig. 6.8, Dr. S. M. Partridge for Figs. 6.5, 6.6 and 6.7, and Dr. R. L. M. Synge, F.R.S., for Fig. 2.12. We are indebted to the proprietors of the *Biochemical Journal* and the Cambridge University Press for permission to publish Figs. 2.12, 3.20 and 6.3–6.8, to the Elsevier Publishing Company for Fig. 7.1, to Brinkmann Instruments, Inc., for Fig. 7.2, to the Locarte Company for Fig. 3.11, to the Reinhold Publishing Corporation for Figs. 4.3 and 4.4, and to the American Association for the Advancement of Science for Fig. 3.19. We are especially grateful to Mr. E. B. Brain for the cover photograph.

The authors would like to thank the publishers and their staff for their help and patience during the preparation of this book. Dr. J. E. Eastoe wishes to thank Professor B. Cohen of the Royal College of Surgeons of England for his advice and encouragement and Mrs. Beryl Eastoe for her painstaking work in preparing the manuscript.

CHAPTER 1

INTRODUCTION

The introduction of new experimental methods is often the main cause for a period of rapid scientific advance. The method of separation of dissolved substances known as chromatography, which forms the subject of this book, has already yielded a rich harvest of discovery in branches of chemistry as different as the separation of isotopes and the purification of new antibiotics. So much new data continues to be accumulated by means of chromatography that at the present time it is certainly the most widely practised, and most fruitful of all the methods which depend on differential migration of the substances under analysis.

Just as the rapid advance of organic chemistry in the nineteenth century was made possible by the techniques of crystallization and distillation, so the great development of biochemistry in the last twenty-five years has depended mainly on extensive application of chromatography and of zone electrophoresis. Like the leading techniques of nineteenth-century organic chemistry, the analytical applications of chromatography are just as important as its use for preparative purposes. Considerable attention will therefore be devoted to both these aspects of the subject in this book.

During the long working period when the average organic chemist was crystallizing and recrystallizing, distilling and redistilling and thus isolating and characterizing many thousands of new substances, a few workers in the applied disciplines allied to organic chemistry were feeling their way towards the new method, now known as chromatography, which was not to be fully exploited for nearly a century. Some reference to the work of these pioneers may be of interest because the discovery of chromatography has often been considered as an outstanding contribution by a single scientist. In fact many aspects of what is today called chromatography were well understood before the time of Mikhial Tswett (1872–1919), the Russian–Italian botanist, who first gave a name to the method. Some notes on the history of chromatography may also serve to emphasize that a technique is not likely to become important until a sufficiency of clearly determined and potentially resolvable problems has made its appearance. Part of Tswett's brilliance was that he found a series of problems specially suited to the chromatographic method. As a botanist he was very interested in the green pigments of leaves. These pigments, which he was the first to separate on a column of calcium carbonate, are still excellent examples for demonstration of the powers of the chromatographic method.

Chromatography, as the name indicates, was evolved for work with coloured substances. An important first stage was described as early as 1850 by Runge who noticed the formation of clearly distinct zones of colour when solutions of certain dyestuffs were dropped on to blotting paper. The procedure must have developed from the method of spot testing in which a drop of the solution to be tested was placed on a specially impregnated piece of paper or cloth. With mixtures of dyes, continuous feeding of the solution into a piece of blotting paper leads to sharper zone formation than after the addition of only a single drop. Such methods were well known among dye technologists during the latter half of the nineteenth century and may well have come to the notice of Tswett. The complete separation of components which is characteristic of modern paper chromatography, was not achieved; for this to take place pure solvent must be allowed to enter the filter paper instead of further amounts of the solution containing the substances to be separated. In modern terms the chromatograms of Runge were examples of the process first examined in detail by Tiselius (1940) and used by him as a quantitative method under the name of *frontal analysis*. As will be described later, *frontal analysis* is applicable when a solution containing more than one solute is allowed to pass through a tube packed with an adsorbent. Since each solute is retarded to a different and characteristic degree, a number of fairly sharp increases in total concentration are observed as the *front* of each solute becomes superimposed on the solution already emerging.

Attempts were made by Reed as early as 1893 to broaden the scope of the method, later to be named chromatography, by using powders packed into glass columns. Unfortunately he was successful only with certain inorganic salts. In quite another field of technology, at only a slightly later date, powders packed into columns were used with much greater success. The American oil chemist, Day, obtained markedly different fractions from natural petroleum after its passage through a column packed with fuller's earth. This work was reported by Day at the First International Petroleum Congress held at Paris in 1900 and was soon confirmed by oil technologists in various parts of Europe. Although these workers used quite large apparatus, including pumps and tubes arranged for sampling at various heights, only the enrichment and not the complete separation of individual components was achieved. Once again, as with Runge's experiments with dyes, no complete separations were possible because the mixed oil was introduced continuously into the column and developing solvent was not used.

The employment of pure solvent for the development of a chromatogram was first described in 1906 by Tswett. Undoubtedly this most important step forward transformed the technique from a potentially useful analytical method into one suitable for qualitative and quantitative analyses and separations on a preparative scale.

Tswett's investigations were not limited to the leaf pigments. In 1910 he described the chromatography of extracts of egg yolk on columns of inulin. Since some of the substances being separated were colourless a means for their detection not based on this property was required. For this purpose Tswett allowed drops of the eluate to evaporate from tissue paper. When fatty substances were present the spots thus formed remained transparent even after evaporation of the solvent. This work laid the basis for identification of colourless components after separation by chromatography. Unfortunately Tswett was not to live long enough to see any considerable spread of his new method. Indeed chromatography was so little known that it is usual to speak of its rediscovery in 1931 by Kuhn and Lederer. The gap between the work of Tswett and this rediscovery was probably due to several factors, mainly well beyond the control of the scientific world. The fact that Tswett's major work was published only in Russian must also have delayed the spread of his ideas. From another point of view, however, the delay can be taken as a measure of how far in advance he was of his scientific contemporaries. For instance, he must certainly have had a rather clear understanding of the process of adsorption, which was the mechanism chiefly concerned in his successful separation of the leaf pigments. Thus he was well aware that an adsorbent after saturation with one substance, can still take up others, and demonstrated this for the leaf pigments with pieces of filter paper from which he was then able to elute the various substances.

Indeed if Tswett's insight into the mechanisms of chromatography had been able to spread more rapidly through the scientific world, as might have happened but for the intervention of the 1914–18 war, the lag period in the history of chromatography might never have occurred. As it was, by 1922 Palmer was able to review considerable chromatographic work on the pigments of milk fat. When in 1931 chromatography began to grow more rapidly it was applied successfully to many of the problems on which Tswett had himself worked. By 1931 Kuhn and Lederer were able to isolate alpha- and beta-carotenes and thus fulfil an earlier prophecy made by Tswett. Many new groups of substances, mainly of natural origin, were then investigated. The size of chromatographic columns was increased so that recovery of the separated materials became practicable. Little improvement in theory or method occurred, however, until 1940–41 when two important steps were taken almost concurrently. In Britain, Martin and Synge (1941) introduced the partition chromatogram, and in Sweden, Tiselius (1940) and Claesson (1946) analysed the three main types of behaviour which take place, either separately or together, during adsorption chromatography.

Many factors now contributed to a very rapid development of the whole subject. Irrespective of their relative importance they may be noted as: (1) the new theoretical treatments due both to Tiselius and to Martin and Synge, (2) the existence of suitable problems, especially for the new technique of partition chromatography, and (3) the simplicity and easy availability of the apparatus needed for partition chromatography on paper.

Once it became possible to carry out chromatographic analyses of complex mixtures of amino acids with nothing more than a glass or wooden box, a trough for organic solvent, filter paper, a sprayer loaded with a solution of ninhydrin, and an oven, the spread of the method became extremely rapid. It may be worthy of mention that one of the observations which led to the development of the first paper chromatogram concerned the great sensitivity of the ninhydrin reaction for amino acids when carried out on filter paper. Since the essential requirements for the successful partition chromatography of water-soluble substances were already known it was then possible to take advantage of filter paper as a matrix for partition chromatography. To the delight of the inventors, the spots of amino acids after such separation, when revealed by heating with ninhydrin, were sharp and well separated and, in certain cases, even showed slight colour differences which were useful for identification. Since as little as 5 μg of a single amino acid or peptide could thus be revealed, a method was at hand for the rapid identification of the very numerous hydrolytic products obtainable from even quite small amounts of proteins. Thus for the first time, a means of attack on the extremely difficult problem of the structure of proteins became available. Any description of its exploitation for the ultimately successful studies of the amino-acid sequences of such molecules as gramicidin S, ACTH, insulin and ribonuclease is beyond the scope of this book. Suffice to mention here that once the relatively easy and rewarding technique of paper chromatography became available, a rather different approach to such problems could sometimes be employed. Instead of starting with the mixture to be analysed and searching for the optimum chromatographic method for each problem, it was often worth while attempting to create problems to fit the method. In the study of amino-acid sequences in proteins, one of the conditions for rapid advance thus became the successful choice of methods of partial hydrolysis which would yield sets of peptides of the right degree of complexity for analysis by paper chromatography. Although many new mixtures of appropriate degrees of complexity were separated in this way, numerous other mixtures remained intractable and so challenged the ingenuity of the analyst. Preliminary separations by electrophoresis or other suitable methods often helped, but a powerful stimulus remained to increase the range and resolving power of the paper chromatogram itself. That this has now been largely achieved is shown by the considerable number of alternative solvent systems which have been described.

In this book, numerous detailed descriptions of well-tried chromatographic systems are given. These should facilitate the separation of many of the mixtures ordinarily encountered in the laboratory. On the other hand, the number of new mixtures still requiring analysis must far exceed all those for which appropriate systems have already been found. Since chromatography, and especially partition chromatography on paper, is a method of analysis which can be varied easily in many different ways it can be expected that numerous modifications and new applications will continue to be found. If in fact this turns out to be true, chromatography will maintain its lead over other methods such as countercurrent solvent extraction, electrophoresis and ultracentrifugation in the sense that more separations of more individual substances will continue to be made in this way.

It is also true that other methods will certainly find many new applications, and powerful new methods will surely be discovered; thus how long chromatography will maintain its leading position can hardly be predicted, although its very convenience must tell in this direction. A safer prediction would perhaps be that the increasingly complex mixtures requiring analysis will need the successive use of several methods rather than the application of any single one.

REFERENCES

Claesson, S. (1946). *Arkiv Kemi Mineral. Geol.* **23A,** 1.
Day, D. T. (1900). *Congr. Intern. pétrole Paris.* **1,** 53.
Kuhn, R. and Lederer, E. (1931). *Naturwiss.* **19,** 306.
Martin, A. J. P. and Synge, R. L. M. (1941). *Biochem. J.* **35,** 1358.
Palmer, L. S. (1922). *Carotinoids and Related Pigments,* Chemical Catalogue Co., New York.
Reed, L. (1893). *Proc. Chem. Soc.* **9,** 123.
Runge, F. F. (1850). *Farbenchemie* **3.**
Tiselius, A. (1940). *Arkiv Kemi Mineral. Geol.* **14B,** 22.
Tswett, M. (1906). *Ber. deut. botan. Ges.* **24,** 316.

CHAPTER 2

PRINCIPLES

Definition and Scope

Chromatography has been defined as 'the technical procedure of analysis by percolation of fluid through a body of comminuted or porous rigid material irrespective of the nature of the physicochemical processes that may lead to the separation of substances in the apparatus' (Gordon, Martin and Synge, 1944). This definition adequately summarizes the main features of the chromatographic technique. It is essentially a practical method for separating the constituents of a mixture, achieved by passage through a system of two phases, which move relative to each other. Normally there is a *stationary phase*, consisting of a finely-divided solid or gel with a large surface area, in contact with a continuous, fluid *moving phase*, which completely fills the interstices. Separation occurs by virtue of differences in the distribution of constituents between the moving phase and either the bulk of the stationary phase or the interface between the two phases.

Initially, the substances to be separated are molecularly dispersed in a small volume of the moving phase. Thus the mixture of solids (or liquids) to be separated is dissolved in the liquid moving phase, or a mixture of their vapours (at a suitable constant temperature) is fed into a stream of carrier gas. The small volume of moving phase, containing the substances to be separated, then passes over the particles of the stationary phase, usually being immediately preceded and followed by the pure moving phase [Fig. 2.1(*a*)]. The dispersed substances would be swept past the stationary phase at the same rate as the moving phase were it not for the fact that there is usually some interaction between these substances and the stationary phase [Fig. 2.1(*b*)]. Their affinity for the stationary phase causes them to travel more slowly than the moving phase, and moreover, where the affinities of the various substances are not the same, they will be transported by the moving phase through the *chromatogram* at different rates [Fig. 2.1(*c*)–(*n*)]. Such differences in the rates of movement are the basis of chromatographic separation.

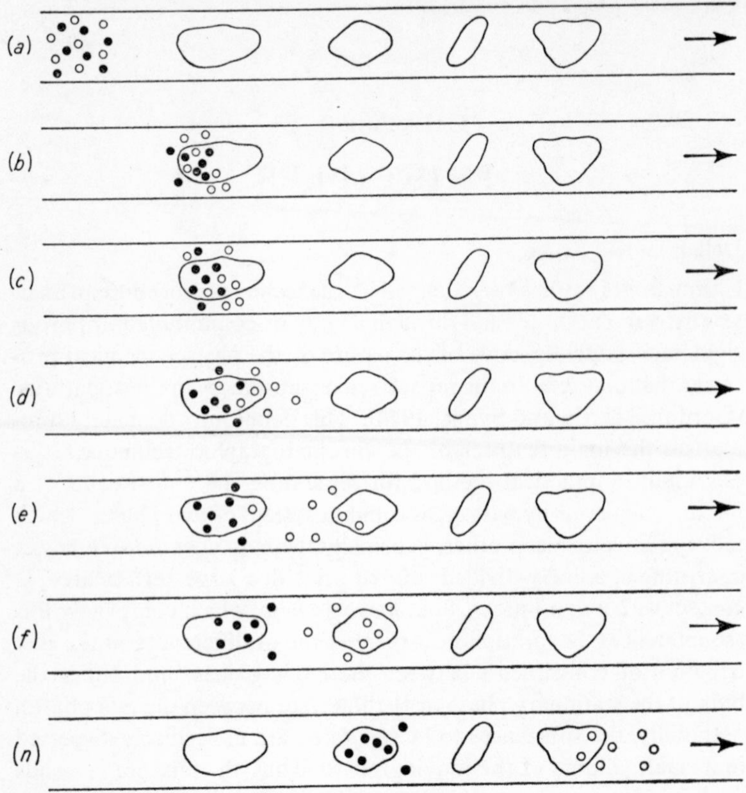

FIG. 2.1. The basis of chromatographic separation.
The affinity of the particles of stationary phase for the black molecules is greater than for the white ones. The white molecules are therefore able to follow the moving solvent more rapidly than the black ones. Separation of the two substances takes place gradually (*b*) to (*f*), being complete at (*n*) where there is pure solvent between the regions containing dissolved substances.

Chromatography provides a versatile method for separation since the choice of materials for both moving and stationary phases is extremely wide. After these have been broadly selected to suit the type of substances to be separated, either phase may be adjusted, as indicated by trial experiments, to give optimum results. Complete separation of substances differing only very slightly in structure may be effected by making the two-phase system, or in practice, the chromatographic *column* of sufficient length.

Differential Migration Methods

Chromatography is only one of a number of methods of separation depending on migration, which has been perfected during the last twenty years. Some features of the most widely used of these differential migration methods, including electrophoresis (electrochromatography or ionography) and multiple partition, which are most closely allied to chromatography, are summarized in Table 2.1.

TABLE 2.1. CHARACTERISTICS OF SOME DIFFERENTIAL MIGRATION METHODS

Method	*Force Causing Migration*	*Property of Substances to be Separated which Provides a Basis for Separation*
Chromatography	Differential movement of two phases due to gravity or pressure	Adsorption* Partition (solubility)* Ion-exchange*
Electrophoresis	Electrical potential gradient	Electrical mobility (charge in relation to molecular size, together with adsorption, partition, etc.)
Liquid–liquid extraction	Stepwise differential movement of two liquid phases	Partition between liquid phases
Mass spectrometry	Magnetic field	Ratio of ionic charge to mass
Differential sedimentation	Centrifugal force	Molecular weight and shape
Diffusion	Thermal agitation	Molecular weight

* Acting singly or in combination.

All these methods are characterized by the action of a driving force which promotes migration of molecules or ions in a permeable medium (solution, gel, gas, or vacuum). The migrating substances also meet with resistive forces which oppose migration. The rate of migration thus depends upon the resultant of the driving and resistive forces. Differences in the value of this resultant force for various substances enable their differential migration and hence separation to take place (Strain, 1960). Migration usually occurs either away from a narrow initial zone of the mixture (chromatography, electrophoresis and differential sedimentation) or in a narrow continuous stream which is made to split up (mass spectrometry or continuous electrophoresis). Generally, differential migration methods are most useful for small quantities of material but become unwieldy on a large scale.

The various methods differ in the nature of the driving and resistive forces and the type of migration medium. The conditions of migration —e.g. temperature, the reactivity of the solvents and adsorbents and the effects of electron bombardment—influence the suitability of the various methods for particular substances. Mass spectrometry and gas chromatography are applicable to all gaseous substances and differential sedimentation is, in principle, suitable for all soluble substances, but is of practical value mainly for those of high molecular weight, i.e. above 10,000. Chromatography, electrophoresis and multiple partition are applicable to a very wide range of soluble substances with both high and low molecular weights.

Apart from broad considerations of molecular weight, solubility and charge, it is very difficult to formulate systematic rules for the selection of the most suitable migration method for the separation of particular mixtures. Practical workers are therefore forced to rely upon analogy, intuition and experience in the application of methods. Furthermore, the expense of the highly specialized equipment required for mass spectrometry and differential centrifugation restricts their use to a minority of laboratories. Chromatography enables complete separations of closely similar substances to be made with very simple and inexpensive equipment. It is the most versatile of the differential migration techniques and has been applied to an enormous range of mixtures of chemical and biochemical interest. Good work can be carried out with cheap home-made equipment which can be modified easily in the light of experience gained in the original construction, to suit experimental requirements during the development of new methods.

Practical aspects of chromatography involving the use of a liquid as the moving phase are discussed in this book. Another volume in this series deals with gas chromatography.

Mechanisms of Chromatography

The driving force causing migration of dissolved or dispersed substances in chromatography is invariably the flow of the moving phase with respect to the stationary one. If this were the only factor operating, all substances would move through the chromatographic system at the same rate as the solvent and therefore would not be separated from one another. The resistive force which opposes migration in chromatography is one of attraction to, or affinity for, the stationary phase and is normally not of the same value for different substances. Thus the components of a mixture are retarded to varying degrees by their affinity for the stationary phase and so are transported by the moving phase at different rates, all of which are less than that of the moving phase itself. Since the attractive forces between dissolved substances and the stationary phase provide the primary basis for chromatographic separations, it is useful to consider their nature, at least in general terms.

The main type of interaction between substances undergoing separation and the stationary phase are described briefly below.

Adsorption. In adsorption chromatography with, for example, calcium phosphate, alumina, or charcoal, as the stationary phase, adsorption is a surface effect which takes place at the boundary between the moving and stationary phases. As a result, a dissolved substance tends to become concentrated in the region close to this surface rather than remaining evenly distributed throughout the liquid phase. This assumes that the stationary phase itself is, for practical purposes, impermeable to such a substance. If the molecules of the solute can penetrate into the particles of the adsorbent, then the concept of an 'internal surface' may be usefully introduced. Adsorption effects characteristically occur at the surface between solids and either liquids or gases. Concentration of hydrogen gas on the extensive surface of finely divided metals of the platinum group, and removal of coloured (aromatic) substances from solution by finely divided carbon (charcoal), are typical adsorption processes. Several types of force can play a part in adsorption, their relative contribution differing in each particular case. Thus the sharing of odd electron pairs, hydrogen-bond formation, orientation of solute molecules with high dipole moments so that the electrostatic field strength is reduced, and van der Waal's forces may be involved. In many systems, several types of force act simultaneously. It should be noted that all the forces, which make separations with the characteristics of adsorption chromatography possible, are weak in comparison with chemical (covalent) bonds and only very rarely cause decomposition of the substance undergoing treatment.

Partition. When the stationary phase consists of droplets of liquid or particles of gel, in which the substances being treated can become dissolved, the separations occur as a result of partition effects. The movement of the substances in the chromatogram is dependent on the relative concentrations in the stationary and moving phases. The dissolved molecules cross and recross the interfacial boundary from the moving to the stationary phase, without becoming concentrated near this surface as happens in adsorption chromatography. The distribution of solute molecules between the two phases will be governed by the *partition law* which states that at constant temperature the ratio of the concentration of solute in one phase to that in the other (known as the *partition coefficient*) will be constant, provided that the system is in equilibrium and that neither phase is saturated with respect to the dissolved substance. Although this law was originally formulated for a closed system which had come to equilibrium, it is also applicable to the conditions found in a chromatogram, although these are continuously changing.

The fate of a substance, X, originally dissolved in the moving phase may be considered. Distribution between the moving phase and that portion of the stationary phase first encountered will occur and the requirements of the partition coefficient will be met, provided that the rate of solvent movement is slow enough for equilibrium conditions to be closely approached. Unless the stationary phase is finely divided, this will occur only at excessively slow rates of flow. As the moving phase progresses through the droplets or particles making up the stationary phase, some of the molecules of substance X will be carried along with it and partition will occur with fresh portions of the stationary phase, which will progressively reduce the concentration for a given portion of the moving phase, the further it penetrates through the stationary phase. The first portion of stationary phase, which initially contained the highest concentration of dissolved solute, will, after a short time, come into contact with less concentrated moving phase, and molecules of X will tend to migrate across the boundary, this time from the stationary to the moving phase, so as to increase the concentration in the latter in accordance with the partition law. The net result is that both the moving solvent front (i.e. the portion of the moving phase initially considered) and the first encountered portion of stationary phase are rapidly depleted of X molecules. Between these regions a sharply defined band of solute, whose molecules repeatedly pass from one phase to the other, follows the moving phase, but at a slower rate.

If a second substance, Y, had been present originally, its partition coefficient being such that its concentration in the moving phase was relatively greater than that of X, a lower concentration of Y would have been held up in that portion of the stationary phase initially in contact with the moving phase. The molecules of Y would have followed the moving solvent more rapidly than those of X and the band of Y would pass more rapidly through the system.

Ion Exchange. In ion-exchange chromatography, the main resistive force is one of electrostatic attraction between electrical charges of one sign, on ions of the migrating substances, and charges of an opposite sign on the stationary phase. The stationary phase is usually an ion-exchange resin, consisting of an insoluble organic framework to which either negatively or positively charged groups are firmly attached by covalent bonds. It is important to notice that, for ion-exchange chromatography to take place, some of the substance to be separated must be at least partially in an ionized form under the conditions (pH, temperature, presence of complex-forming reagents, etc.) existing in the chromatographic system.

Molecular Sieving. Certain substances, such as the starches, are very porous, each granule being a microsponge with a complex system of holes of the same order of size as molecules. When a material of this type forms the stationary phase of a chromatogram, the possibility arises of separating substances with molecules too large to penetrate the pores, from others of smaller molecular size, which can freely diffuse in and out. The latter are preferentially retarded compared with the former so that the smaller molecules move through the chromatographic system more slowly. This process, which is known as *molecular sieving* or *gel filtration*, was first demonstrated with chromatograms of potato starch by Lathe and Ruthven (1956).

Recently a cross-linked derivative of the polysaccharide, dextran, has been made available commercially under the name Sephadex (see page 179). It is a granular, hydrophilic, water-insoluble material which is non-ionic and swells considerably in the aqueous solutions in which it is normally used. It is available in several forms, differing in degree of cross-linkage and hence pore size. Sephadex thus has considerable advantages over starch for controlled gel filtration. It can be used both in batches and in chromatographic columns to separate molecules of different sizes. If one of two substances has molecules which are too large to enter the pores of the Sephadex, and the volume inside the granules which can be reached by the other, is known, then the amount of Sephadex required for a given separation can be calculated. The rapid removal of salt from solutions of large molecules is an application of this kind.

Ion-exchange resins are normally porous, a high proportion of the ionizable groups being inside the grains of solid. For this reason molecular-sieve effects, in addition to interaction between charged groups, are of practical importance in ion-exchange chromatography.

Classification of Chromatographic Methods

A classification of chromatographic methods based on the mechanism by which separation occurs would, at first sight, appear to be most satisfactory since it would bring together techniques based on common modes of action. Unfortunately, in the majority of chromatographic systems, more than one type of mechanism occurs and it is often difficult to establish which one predominates under defined conditions. Thus, the controversy as to whether partition or adsorption is more important in the separation of amino acids on starch is still unsettled, and it would seem likely that what actually occurs is a complex combination of both mechanisms.

In the chromatography of amino acids on ion-exchange resins, adsorption, partition and molecular sieving effects all play an important part in the separations, in addition to electrostatic interaction between ion and resin. If chromatographic methods are initially classified strictly according to mechanism, this would involve repetition of the description of many individual separations.

An initial classification according to the state of the moving phase into *gas* and *liquid* (or solution) *chromatography* is useful and not ambiguous, except that the latter term is used in a wider sense than that of Reichstein and van Euw (1938). Their 'liquid or flowing chromatogram' could perhaps be more usefully described as an *elution* method (see page 24). Further subdivision can be made according to the nature of the stationary phase. Thus there are gas–liquid and gas–solid systems and, in systems depending upon flow of liquid, many specialized techniques such as *paper chromatography* and *resin chromatography*, in which filter paper and ion-exchange resin respectively form the stationary phase.

Finally, different experimental techniques must often be distinguished, particularly with regard to the method of carrying out the elution in liquid chromatography, e.g. *frontal analysis, displacement development, carrier elution* and *gradient elution* methods, considering them in order of increasing value for bringing about separations. In Table 2.2 are listed most of the chromatographic methods already referred to and some others which fall outside the scope of this book.

TABLE 2.2. CLASSIFICATION OF CHROMATOGRAPHIC METHODS

Moving Phase	*Stationary Phase*	*Mechanism*	*Substances Capable of Separation*	*Special Features*
Gas	Liquid on inert support	Partition	All volatile substances	Rapidity of separation
	Solid	Adsorption		
Liquid	Liquid a. on inert support	Primarily partition with adsorption and diffusion effects important	Substances soluble in both moving and stationary phases	Simplicity of equipment for paper chromatography
,,	b. in a gel			
,,	c. in paper*			
,,	Solid a. 'adsorbent'	Adsorption, ion exchange	Soluble, adsorbable substances	Variety of elution techniques: 1. Frontal analysis 2. Displacement development 3. Carrier displacement 4. Succession of solvents of increasing eluting power 5. Gradient elution
,,	b. ion-exchange resin	Ion exchange, molecular sieve, adsorption	Simple ions, zwitterions and ionizable macromolecules	
,,	c. modified cellulose*	Primarily partition and ion exchange		

* Separation of paper and modified-cellulose chromatography into liquid–liquid and liquid–solid groups respectively is arbitrary. Both forms are related and show features in common.

Examples of Two Important Types of Chromatogram

Further discussion of the principles underlying chromatographic procedures will be aided by a preliminary description of two basic

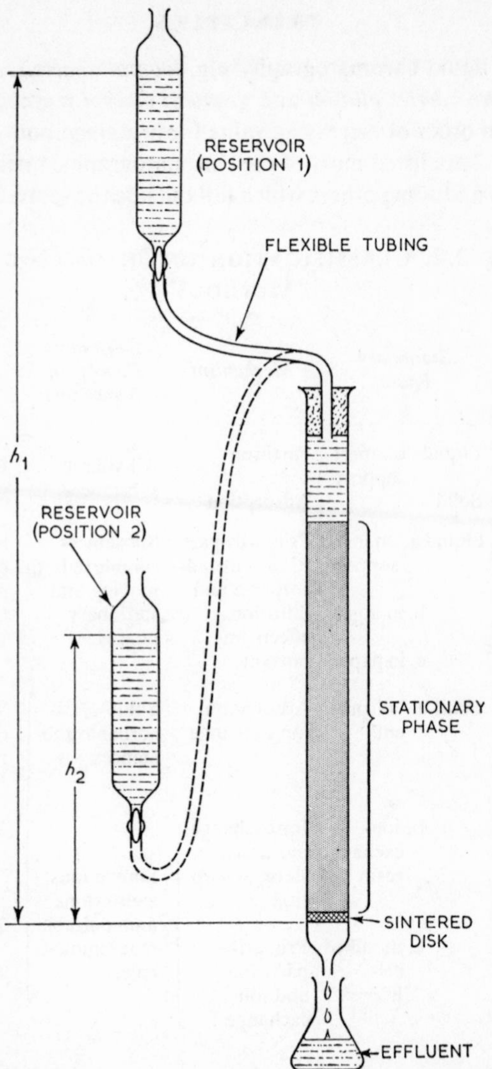

FIG. 2.2. Chromatography column with solvent reservoir connected by flexible plastic tubing. The moving phase flows past the stationary phase which forms a column in the vertical tube. The rate of flow due to gravity is proportional to the height (h) of the meniscus of the liquid in the reservoir above the sintered disk at the base of the column. By lowering the reservoir from position 1 to position 2 (which may be below the top of the column) the flow rate is decreased in the ratio h_2 to h_1.

types of system in popular use. These differ not only in the general appearance of the apparatus, but also in the nature of the force which causes the moving phase to flow through the stationary phase.

Column Chromatography. A glass tube, normally vertical or nearly so, is packed with particles of the stationary phase, which rest upon a rigid but porous support (e.g. a sintered-glass plate or glass-wool pad) at the bottom of the tube, to prevent further movement of the stationary phase in a downward direction (Fig. 2.2). The space between

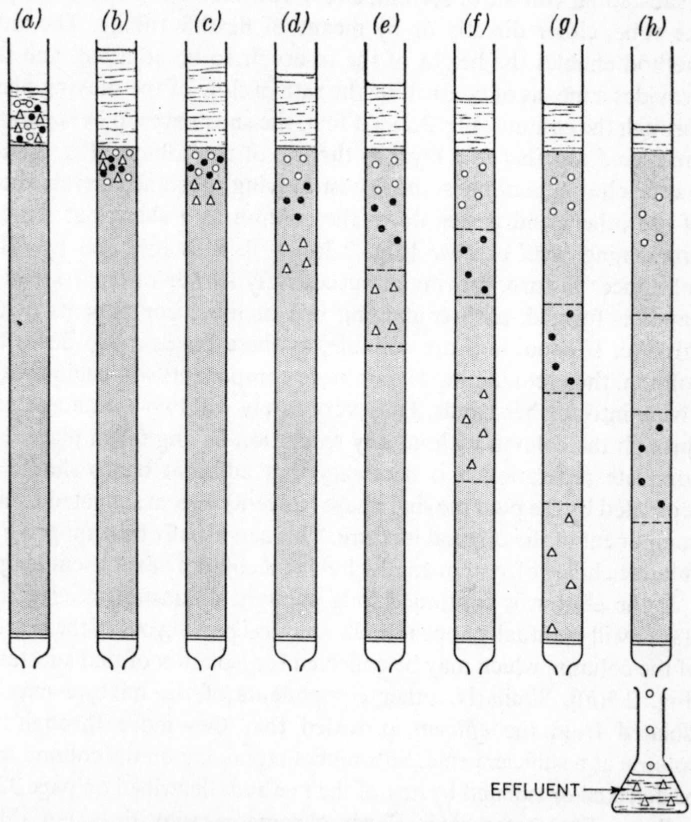

FIG. 2.3. Separation of the components of a mixture by column chromatography. The mixture of substances added in solution percolates into the top of the column of stationary phase (*a*), more solvent is then added (*b*). The different substances travel down the column at different rates (*b*) to (*h*). A distinct zone of the fastest moving substance (represented by triangles) has become separated at (*e*) and appears in the effluent at (*h*). This will be followed by pure solvent before the second component (black circles) emerges.

the particles is completely filled with a liquid which moves under the influence of gravity and can pass out at the bottom through the porous support. A solution of the mixture of substances to be separated, dissolved in a small volume of the liquid phase, is added just above the top of the *column* of stationary phase and allowed to sink in. When the liquid level has fallen to the top of the stationary phase, the empty upper portion of the tube is filled with a further quantity of the eluting solvent (moving phase) and, if the separation requires a substantial volume of solvent, a reservoir is connected to the top of the tube, either directly or by means of flexible tubing. The latter method enables the height of the reservoir to be adjusted, and this provides a means of controlling the rate of flow of the moving phase through the column (Fig. 2.2). At first, the substances to be separated are mixed together in a layer at the top of the column [Fig. 2.3(*a*)]. As the elution continues, the fastest-moving substance travels ahead of the others and passes down the column as a sharp but steadily broadening *band* or *zone* [Fig. 2.3(*e*)–(*g*)]. It is followed by other substances in turn, moving at successively slower rates. A series of bands is formed, each containing one or more components of the mixture. If conditions are suitable, as these bands move down the column, those containing two or more components will begin to subdivide into further bands. Only very rarely will two substances pass through the column without any resolution having taken place. For complete separation it is necessary that adjacent bands should be separated by the pure moving phase (solvent) uncontaminated by any component of the original mixture. This can usually be arranged by a suitable choice of system and by having a column of sufficient length.

If the elution is continued long enough, the fastest-moving substance will eventually appear in the solution passing out of the bottom of the column, which may be collected for isolation of that substance [Fig. 2.3(*h*)]. Similarly, other components of the mixture may be isolated from the *effluent*, provided that they move through the column at a sufficient rate. Substances remaining on the column may be detected or isolated by any of the methods described on page 32.

Paper Chromatography. Paper chromatography does not differ from column chromatography in any one essential principle. The practical differences, which are considerable, all stem from the mechanical properties of paper which, unlike powders, does not require a container for support. Paper in the form of strips or sheets can be maintained easily in a vertical position by attachment to a support from which it can hang. Alternatively, rolls of paper are rigid enough to stand without additional support. In column procedures, the solution containing the substances to be separated is allowed to soak into the flat upper surface of the packed adsorbent or other powder from which the chromatogram has been made; this is necessary because it is the only surface of the adsorbent which is not in contact with the containing tube. Since, however, the whole surface of a paper chromatogram is exposed, the solution to be analysed can be applied at any particular point. It is normally placed near one edge of the paper only because the advancing solvent front can then carry the substances being separated over most of the length of the paper. Because filter paper is relatively thin, no difficulties due to uneven distribution through the thickness of the paper are ever encountered. This is a considerable advantage over column chromatography in which skewed or tipped bands are commonplace, mainly because of uneven packing of the adsorbent.

In paper chromatography the solvent moves through the paper by capillarity or, in a descending system in which the paper has been completely saturated with solvent, by gravitational flow. Consequently the flow rate cannot be altered as it can be in column chromatography, by variation in the pressure at which the solvent is supplied. In practice this is not a disadvantage because the flow rates of the solvents actually used are slow enough for the attainment of equilibrium between the moving and stationary phases and thus for the formation of sharp spots. Solvent flow rates on paper chromatograms are determined by two main factors which are, in order of importance, (1) the viscosity of the solvent and (2) the texture of the filter paper. As will be mentioned later the coarser papers are not very suitable for paper chromatography because the spots formed on them are too diffuse.

Since paper chromatograms are not closely surrounded by a container in contact with the paper and because volatile solvents are used, the tendency to lose solvent from the paper by evaporation must be checked. This is achieved by placing the paper and its supply of solvent inside a relatively air-tight box. Once the atmosphere in this box has become saturated with the solvents being used, evaporation from the paper will no longer occur. When very volatile solvents such as ether, are being used, a period for preliminary equilibration, as well as careful lagging of the box, is necessary. Unless the lagging is adequate, local changes of temperature will cause evaporation of solvent from one part of the paper and condensation on another with consequent serious distortion of the pattern of spots.

It is true that if the development of a paper chromatogram were continued for a sufficient time the separated spots would run to the edge and ultimately drip off the paper but this is not a practical method of working. The main difficulty is that resolution of spots becomes poor near the bottom edge of the paper owing to the formation of a pool of the moving phase. The size of this pool, of course, fluctuates as a result of drop formation; furthermore, if the spots were allowed to run off the paper they could not be revealed by means of colour reagents, the use of which makes paper chromatography such a convenient technique.

For these reasons paper chromatograms are terminated when the substances undergoing separation are spread well down the paper but before the fastest-moving one has reached the bottom edge. At this stage the paper is dried to remove solvent and sprayed with or dipped into an appropriate revealing reagent as will be described in detail on page 106.

Application of the Mixture Requiring Separation to the Chromatographic System

Two methods have been used for adding mixtures of substances to chromatographic systems. The first of these is generally useful since, at least in principle, it permits the complete separation of all the components. A limited quantity of the mixture (which for quantitative work requires to be accurately known), dissolved in a relatively small volume of solvent, is added at the beginning of the experiment. Subsequently, the pure moving phase, which should not contain any of the components of the mixture, is allowed to pass through the system continuously in order to *develop the chromatogram*. Initially the mixture to be separated is situated near the point of application but, if its components move at different rates, each substance forms a sharp zone which soon begins to separate from those substances immediately preceding and following it. If development of the chromatogram is stopped before anything but pure solvent has left the system, then the various substances may be observed spatially separated at different levels on the chromatogram. This technique is almost invariably applied to paper chromatography and is sometimes used with columns.

Alternatively, in *elution chromatography*, development may be carried on for a longer period and the solution leaving the chromatographic system (*eluate* or *effluent*) collected in a large number of consecutive portions (*fractions*), which are subsequently analysed. Figure 2.4 shows a typical *elution curve* in which the concentrations of substances present in the eluate are plotted against the volume which has run out of the column. It can be seen that each substance emerges as a zone with a single *peak* of concentration. In each peak

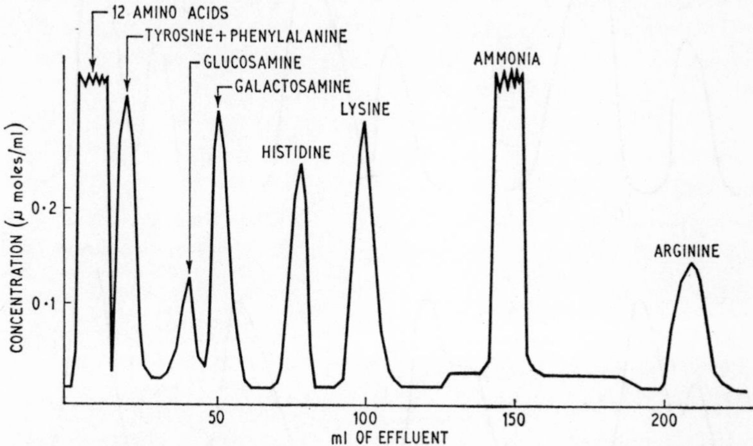

FIG. 2.4. Elution diagram of a mixture of amino sugars and basic amino acids from a hydrolysate of a protein-polysaccharide complex from bone. The amino sugars, glucosamine and galactosamine, are separated completely from the amino acids and almost completely from each other. The basic amino acids, histidine, lysine and arginine, are also completely resolved. Near the beginning of the curve, tyrosine and phenylalanine emerge mixed together and before this is a large peak containing twelve amino acids, which the column has failed to resolve.

the concentration rises to a maximum and then falls to zero where, ideally, it remains for several fractions before rising again in the next peak. Near the beginning of the elution diagram in Fig. 2.4 a number of substances emerge as a single peak, the resolving power of the particular system being insufficient for separation. Partial separation is shown by the overlapping of successive peaks in the elution diagram (Fig. 2.5).

The second method of application of the mixture for chromatography is to run it on continuously for the whole period of the experiment, instead of following the mixture being analysed with pure solvent. This method of working formed the basis of the earliest types of chromatogram, but as already pointed out, it severely restricted their scope, since separation of pure substances is not possible except for part of the fastest-moving component. The technique was subsequently re-introduced by Tiselius (1940) and is known as *frontal analysis*. Employed in this way, it became a valuable analytical tool which helped to elucidate the mechanisms involved in

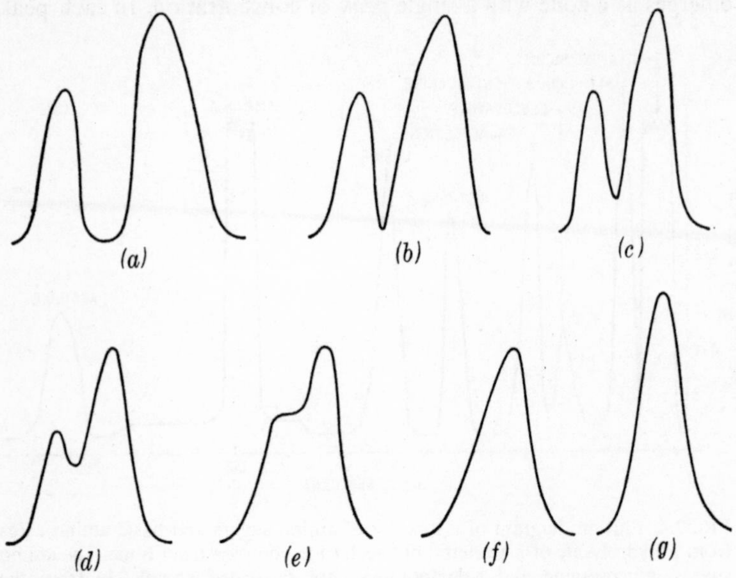

FIG. 2.5. Appearance of adjacent peaks in an elution curve with various degrees of overlapping.

(*a*) Complete separation.
(*b*) Marginal separation.
(*c*) Slight overlap.
(*d*) Overlap, trough still visible.
(*e*) Flat portion, no trough.
(*f*) Asymmetrical single peak (slope less on leading edge).
(*g*) Complete overlap.

column chromatography. For this purpose the concentration of the effluent from the column is monitored continuously by an optical method which measures changes in refractive index by the 'schlieren' method of Toepler. The concentration, which is initially zero, rises in a series of *steps* (Fig. 2.6) each of which is the *front* of one of the components. Once a substance has emerged from the column, its concentration in the effluent remains constant and equal to that in the original solution. The height of each step is therefore a measure of the concentration of a particular substance, whereas the volume of liquid emerging from the column before the step, is characteristic of the substance itself (whatever its concentration) and may help to identify its presence in a mixture of unknown composition. The *specific retention volume* or *retardation volume* of a substance has been

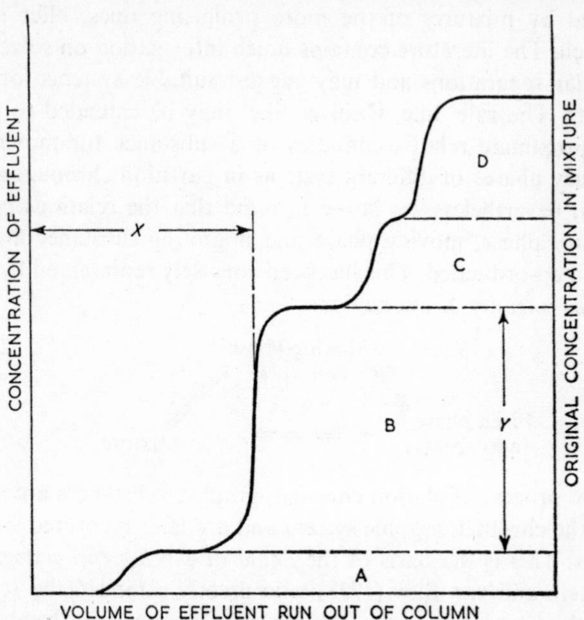

FIG. 2.6. Frontal analysis curve for a mixture of four substances A, B, C, D. Distance *X* represents the retardation volume of substance B. Distance *Y* represents the concentration of substance B in the original solution.

defined as the volume of liquid passing through the column per gram of adsorbent before that substance leaves the column. In the final state, the composition of the effluent is the same as that of the solution entering the column.

Development of Chromatograms

Success in carrying out particular separations in chromatography frequently depends upon judicious choice of solvent for the moving phase, having regard both to the substances to be separated and to the stationary phase. Often the choice is limited by the chemical nature or lability of the substances being separated and the selection of the moving phase (often a multi-component mixture) is the main available variable for the investigator attempting difficult separations.

As yet it is difficult to lay down general rules concerning choice of solvent, but systematic experimental trials with simple solvents, followed by mixtures of the more promising ones, offer a basic approach. The literature contains much information on solvents for particular separations and may suggest suitable systems for initial attempts. The rule 'like dissolves like' may be extended to predict the approximate relative affinities of a substance for moving and stationary phases of different systems in partition chromatography. It must, nevertheless, be borne in mind that the relations between stationary phase, moving phase and migrating substance are complex and co-ordinated. This has been concisely represented by Strain (1960) as a trinity of interactions.

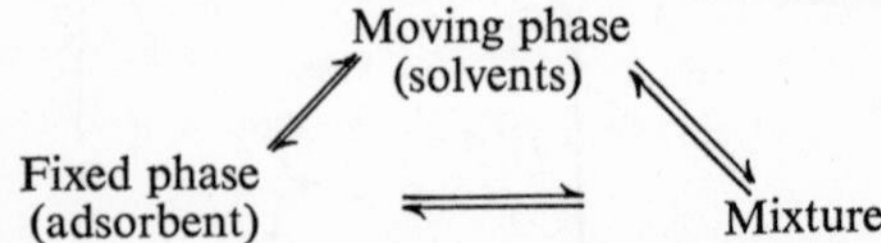

In the process of elution chromatography, substances are washed out of the chromatographic system and are later recovered from the solvents. This is the basis of the *liquid* or *flowing chromatogram* of Reichstein and van Euw (1938) who greatly extended the scope of the method by washing the column with a series of solvents of increasing *eluting power* and collecting these solvents separately. Change of solvent is necessary because if elution is continued for a long period with a single solvent, successive substances are eluted from the column in increasing volumes of solvent at decreasing concentrations. Their peaks on an elution diagram become lower and flatter (see Fig. 6.3). Eventually, substances may remain on the column which move at such a slow rate that elution would require larger volumes of solvent than are practical. Such difficulties may be avoided since a suitable change of solvent will result in rapid elution of slow-moving substances and will give sharp peaks on the elution diagram.

In chromatographic systems where adsorption plays a significant part (e.g. with alumina as stationary phase), eluting power increases approximately as the dielectric constant of the solvent, so that a series of solvents, e.g. aliphatic hydrocarbons, aromatic hydrocarbons, ether, chloroform, organic esters, alcohols, water and organic acids, and bases, shows successive increases in eluting power (see Chapter 4). Lists of solvents in order of eluting power are not necessarily applicable to any given substance, since the precise order varies with the substances being eluted and the experimental conditions. Such lists are useful as an approximate guide. In systems where ion-exchange plays an important part, change of the pH or ionic strength of the buffer solutions used for elution often allows very precise control of the relative rates of movement of different substances.

Irregular Zone Formation and 'Tailing'

A practical problem which frequently arises in chromatography is to prevent the deterioration of a compact and well-defined zone, which would give a sharp peak on an elution graph, into a diffuse zone of irregular shape, during the course of development of the chromatogram. Two effects, arising from entirely different causes, may be distinguished as playing important parts in zone deterioration and the consequent loss of resolution of neighbouring substances on chromatograms.

Irregular zone formation arises primarily from a lack of homogeneity in the distribution of particles of different sizes in the stationary phase. Normally the material used for pouring a column includes particles having a range of sizes. If the solid settles under gravity with a slow flow of solvent in a vertical tube, the particles tend to become distributed with the larger ones towards the bottom and the smaller ones nearer the top of the column. This vertical heterogeneity has no adverse effect provided that the particle size in each horizontal plane throughout the column is uniform (i.e. only random variations occur between neighbouring particles), when it is said to be isoporous. If the column is disturbed while settling or is not poured evenly, the average particle size may vary at different places in the same horizontal plane. Then during the development of such a chromatogram, the solvent will travel more rapidly through areas where the average particle size is greatest and will carry some of each dissolved substance through that part of the column at a greater rate than the rest of the zone. Such irregularity of column packing therefore results in the formation of curved, sloping or irregular bands of the substances undergoing separation and consequently a deterioration in shape of the peaks in the elution diagram (Fig. 2.7). Drake (1949) has shown that this irregular zone formation becomes progressively more pronounced with increase of column diameter. Because of these effects the sharpest fronts are obtainable with long narrow columns and low rates of flow.

The second effect causing zone spreading is usually called *tailing*

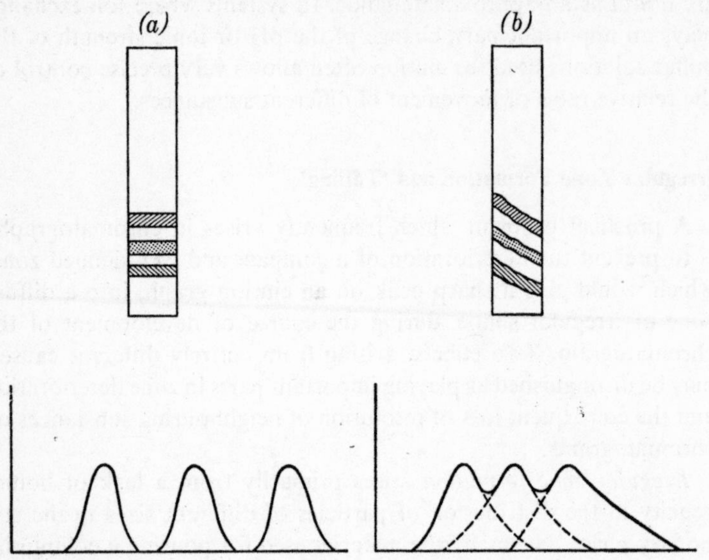

FIG. 2.7. Shape of bands and elution curves in (*a*) isoporous and (*b*) non-isoporous columns.

and is characterized by a very gradual fall in concentration of a substance following its region of maximum concentration. The peak in the elution diagram is followed by a long 'tail' which represents elution in very low concentration [Fig. 2.8(*a*)].

This effect has several disadvantages:

(1) A very large volume of eluate must be collected to recover all the substance.

(2) Complete separation from another more slowly moving substance may be unobtainable or, in analytical work, it may not be possible to assess the true base line between the peaks [Fig. 2.8(*b*)].

(3) If the eluting solvent is changed and the new solvent emerges from the column while the tail is being eluted a small spurious peak may result [Fig. 2.8(*c*)].

Tailing may also occur in paper chromatography. The normally compact circular spot then shows a long tail of gradually decreasing intensity, like a comet [Fig 2.8(*d*)].

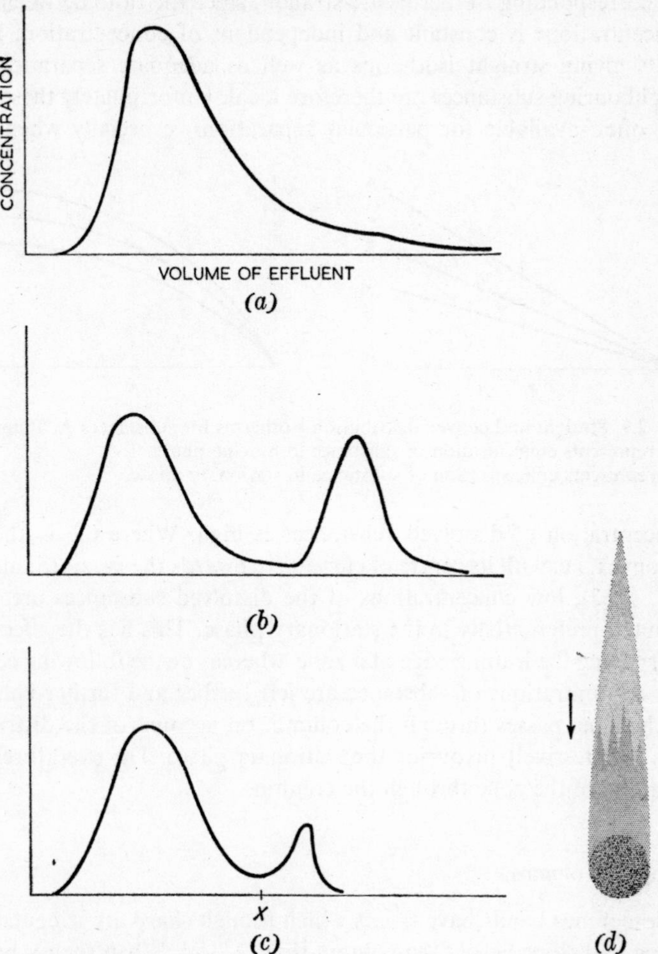

FIG. 2.8. Tailing Effects.
In (*c*) the new solvent emerges from the column at point X.

Tailing takes place when the distribution of a substance undergoing chromatographic separation between the moving and stationary phases, has a particular type of concentration dependence. This distribution is most conveniently expressed in the form of a *distribution isotherm* in which the concentration *y* in the stationary phase is plotted against the equilibrium concentration *x* in the moving phase at constant temperature (Fig. 2.9). With sharp zones, the corresponding isotherms are straight, since the ratio between the concentrations is constant and independent of concentration. Solvents giving straight isotherms as well as adequate separation of neighbouring substances are therefore ideal. Unfortunately these are not often available for particular separations, especially when the

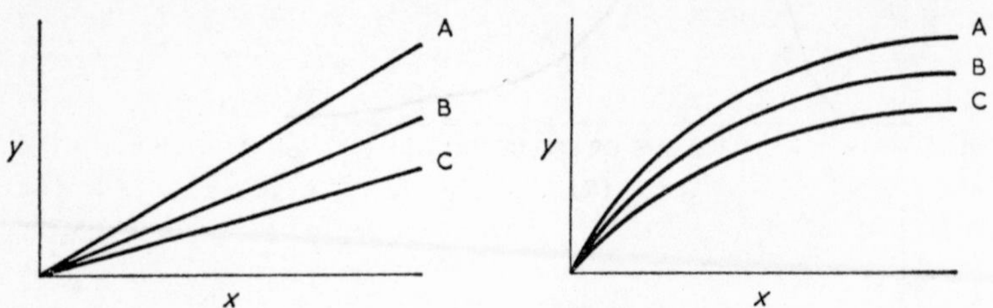

FIG. 2.9. Straight and convex distribution isotherms for substances A, B and C.
x represents concentration of substance in moving phase.
y represents concentration of substance in stationary phase.

concentration of dissolved substances is high. Where the isotherm is convex, i.e. with its centre of curvature towards the *x*-axis (Samuelson, 1952), low concentrations of the dissolved substances are distributed preferentially in the stationary phase. This has the effect of sharpening the leading edge of a zone, whereas on the following edge, low concentrations of substance are left further and further behind as the zone passes through the column, on account of the distribution progressively favouring the stationary phase. The overall result is tailing of the zone through the column.

Coupled Columns

Sometimes bands have fronts which though sharp are irregular in shape and slope across the column [Fig. 2.7(*b*)]. When such a band reaches the bottom of the column, the emerging liquid consists of a mixture of pure solvent from one part of the lowest cross-section and the solution of the substance in the band from the remainder of the above cross-section. The result is a loss of resolution and possibly mixing of successive bands. Although the undesirable effects of irregular zone formation can be greatly reduced by using long, narrow columns, these suffer from the limitations of being awkward to pack and having a limited capacity for the mixture undergoing separation. Claesson (1947) and Hagdahl (1948) worked out an ingenious method of obtaining both sharp fronts and high capacity by making use of the characteristics of convex-distribution isotherms, which are of common occurrence. A narrow column is joined below a wide one, with a mixing chamber containing only liquid between them (see Fig. 4.4). When the first portion of dissolved substance from an irregular front reaches the mixing chamber, it mixes with the pure solvent already there so that the solution entering the narrower column is at first very dilute. The substance is therefore preferentially distributed in the stationary phase because of its low concentration and the convex shape of the distribution isotherm (Fig. 2.9). The substance entering initially is soon overtaken by the bulk of the material and a new, sharp, and regular front is formed. This may become irregular during its passage through the second column, but the effect is less marked because of the smaller column diameter. Recently, Hagdahl (1954) described a standard series of coupled columns decreasing progressively in both diameter and length, with each column one half of the volume of the one above it. The coupled-column method is probably of greatest value for frontal analysis and displacement chromatography but also has the effect of sharpening the leading edges of peaks in elution chromatography. Partridge and Brimley (1951) found coupled columns useful for displacement chromatography using ion-exchange resins.

Gradient Elution

The marked effect of changing the moving phase from a solvent of comparatively low eluting power to one of a higher power, both on the rate of migration of substances and on the sharpness of the eluted peaks, has been mentioned. With completely miscible solvents, instead of making the change instantaneously at one particular point in the development of the chromatogram, the composition of the eluting solvent may be changed gradually and continuously with time, so that initially it has the composition of the first solvent and finally it consists of the pure second solvent, having passed meanwhile through all the intermediate mixtures. This is known as *gradient elution* since there is a continuous gradient of composition throughout the change (Fig. 2.10).

Each substance, therefore, can be eluted by solvent of a composition close to the optimum for giving both a sharply defined zone and a reasonably fast migration rate. For this to occur, the correct gradient must be selected and it must be applied at the optimum point in the development. Furthermore, gradient elution is a powerful means of combating the tailing of substances resulting from

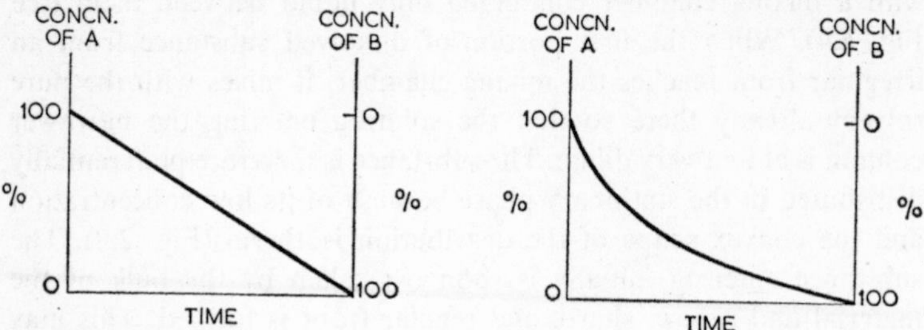

FIG. 2.10. Linear and exponential changes in solvent composition for gradient elution.

convex isotherms. The material in low concentration following the bulk of a substance, instead of being progressively more favourably distributed in the stationary phase as it falls behind, finds itself in a region which favours distribution in the moving phase, owing to the gradient in the composition of the solvent. The overall effect is to sharpen the trailing edge of the zone. The front edge is sharpened even further by this process aiding the effect of the convex isotherm.

Displacement Development

Another method of developing chromatograms was introduced by Tiselius (1943) with the object of minimizing the tailing of substances through the column. In this technique, the moving phase is a solution of a substance which has a higher affinity for the stationary phase than any of the substances being separated. Under these conditions, the substances undergoing separation displace one another, the back of each zone being sharp (Fig. 2.11) and the displacing agent emerging last of all. Each substance rapidly attains a characteristic stationary concentration, represented by the height of the step in the elution curve. The method has the serious practical disadvantage that the substances leave the column continuously without any intermediate volumes of pure solvent.

A modified form of this method, known as *carrier displacement*, uses carrier substances with intermediate affinities for the stationary phase. During development, these run in between the components of the mixture being investigated and in this way separate them.

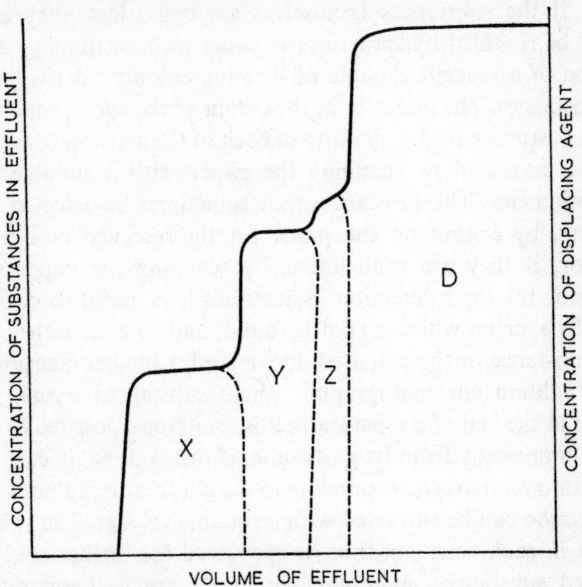

FIG. 2.11. Displacement of substances X, Y and Z by displacing agent D.

Homologous aliphatic acids have been separated by using their methyl esters as carriers. For separations of this type to be of practical use, marked differences must exist in some property, e.g. volatility, between the substances undergoing separation and the carriers.

Detection and Determination of Substances Following Chromatography

The chromatographic process itself merely serves to separate the components of a mixture. To be of practical value, at least with colourless substances, either the individual substances must be isolated in a pure state or their presence must be established by any appropriate method. Often the amount of each substance needs to be determined as accurately as possible. Some method of detecting the location and chemical nature of the separated substances is therefore an essential adjunct to chromatography. The technique used necessarily varies according to whether the substances are allowed to stay in the chromatographic system or are collected in the effluent.

In paper chromatography, the separated substances normally remain in the chromatographic system as compact spots on the dried paper. If the substances themselves are colourless, they can very simply be revealed by spraying the paper with, or dipping it into, a solution of a reagent capable of forming coloured derivatives with the substances. The intensity of the colour of the spots, which in turn gives an estimate of the quantity of each of the separated substances, may be measured by scanning the paper with a suitable type of absorptiometer. The substances may sometimes be detected without spraying, by examining the paper for fluorescence in ultra-violet light, or, if they are radioactive, by scanning the paper with an apparatus for their detection. Sometimes it is useful to cut out the area of paper on which a spot is found, and to elute either the original substance or the coloured derivative for further measurements.

For column chromatography, where substances remain on the column at the end of a separation, it is sometimes possible to extrude the column neatly from its glass tube. If this is done, it can then be cut up into sections corresponding to the chromatographic zones and each section can be extracted with a suitable solvent. The substances present in each zone can thus be recovered for further study. With coloured substances, assuming the bands are well separated and regularly shaped, it is easy to decide where to divide the column. Colourless substances may sometimes be detected by their fluorescence or radioactivity or alternatively by the use of suitable reagents, which are either streaked along the extruded column in a narrow line or are applied to small portions of material, removed with a microspatula.

Where the separated substances leave the chromatographic system dissolved in the moving phase, the effluent may either be monitored continuously for any property characteristic of the separated band, or collected in successive fractions of constant volume. Standard methods of analysis can be used to detect and determine the amounts of the substances in the fractions, either in solution or after removal of the solvent. Continuously-recording devices are available to measure refractive index, pH, conductivity, absorption of ultraviolet radiation, colour produced with an automatically added reagent or titratable acidity or basicity of the solution, as it emerges from the column.

Quantitative Theories of Chromatographic Behaviour

A number of theories of chromatography have been put forward in an attempt to correlate as completely as possible the behaviour of substances in chromatographic systems with their chemical structure or other well-defined properties. While some success has been achieved in giving an approximate explanation of what is observed experimentally, it is by no means possible to predict with certainty the behaviour of a new and untried system. This largely results from the existence of various mechanisms of unknown relative importance, all acting simultaneously. Chromatography therefore remains a practical technique with some systematic background, rather than a highly quantitized branch of physical chemistry. Some elementary concepts which may assist the practical worker to visualize and possibly, in certain cases, to predict what will occur in his experiments are given below.

The R Value. Under given conditions, a particular substance will migrate in a chromatographic system at a definite rate compared with the rate of the moving phase. The ratio of the rate of movement of the substance in the chromatogram to that of the moving phase in the upper part of the tube which is filled only with solvent, is defined as the R value of that substance in that particular system and at the prevailing temperature. If the eluting solvent is allowed to flow for a given time and at a constant rate, the ratio of these rates will be equal to the ratio of the distances moved by the substance and the upper meniscus of the moving phase, respectively.

$$R = \frac{\text{rate of movement of the migrating substance down the tube}}{\left[\begin{array}{c}\text{rate of movement of moving phase}\\ \text{in the tube above the stationary phase}\end{array}\right]}$$

$$= \frac{\text{distance travelled by substance}}{\left[\begin{array}{c}\text{distance travelled by upper meniscus}\\ \text{of moving phase in the same time}\end{array}\right]}$$

The R_f value. In paper chromatography, the rate of movement of the solvent front is easily observed as the solvent advances through and wets the paper. In any chromatogram the rate of movement of the solvent in that part of the system not containing the stationary phase is slower than where the stationary phase is present. This is because the rates in the two parts of the system are inversely proportional to the corresponding cross-sectional areas available for solvent.

Where the solid phase is present, the relevant cross-sectional area is that of the column minus the cross-sectional area of the solid phase.

Because of the ease with which the movement of the solvent front can be measured, the distance moved by the spots on paper chromatograms is always related to it, the ratio being known as the R_f value. This concept may also be usefully applied in column chromatography where the rate or distance of movement of the solvent within the two-phase system is considered.

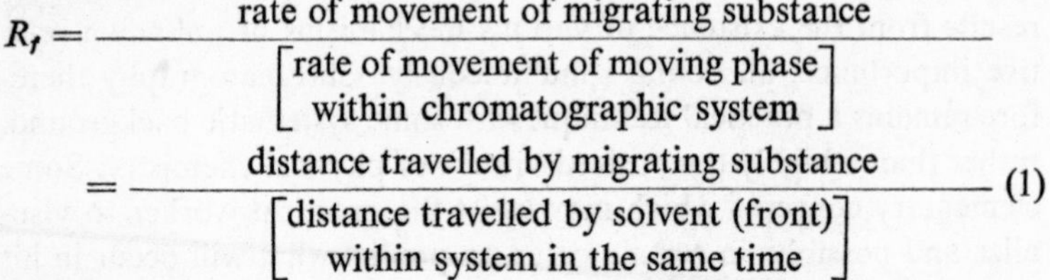

$$R_f = \frac{\text{rate of movement of migrating substance}}{\left[\begin{matrix}\text{rate of movement of moving phase} \\ \text{within chromatographic system}\end{matrix}\right]}$$

$$= \frac{\text{distance travelled by migrating substance}}{\left[\begin{matrix}\text{distance travelled by solvent (front)} \\ \text{within system in the same time}\end{matrix}\right]} \quad (1)$$

Relation Between the R_f Value and the Distribution Coefficient. The idea of the partition coefficient, already mentioned in connection with the partition of a solute in equilibrium between two liquid phases in contact, can be extended to cover the distribution of a molecularly dispersed substance between the fluid moving phase and either a solid or liquid stationary phase such as is used in chromatography. By defining concentrations on the basis of the total weight of migrating substance present in or associated with the stationary and moving phases respectively, it is possible to give a practical definition of a distribution coefficient α which is useful for describing the behaviour of substances in chromatographic systems, whether the mechanism be partition, adsorption, ion-exchange, etc. or a combination of all three.

$$\alpha = \frac{\left[\begin{matrix}\text{weight of substance associated with unit} \\ \text{volume of stationary phase}\end{matrix}\right]}{\text{weight of substance, per unit volume of moving phase}}$$

The value of α can be determined by experiments on a limited two-phase system which has reached equilibrium at constant temperature.

A relation between α and the R_f value may be derived as follows. In a chromatographic system,

let A_s be the average area of cross-section of the stationary phase,
let A_m be the average area of cross-section of the moving phase,
($A_s + A_m = A_t$ the total area of cross-section of the system, e.g. column).

Suppose that a volume V of the moving phase flows through (i.e. both into and out of) the system at a sufficiently slow rate for equilibrium to be preserved with regard to the distribution of a migrating substance between the phases.

Distance travelled by migrating substance

$$= \frac{V}{\text{effective area of cross-section over which distribution can occur}}$$

$$= \frac{V}{A_m + \alpha A_s} \qquad (2)$$

Distance travelled by moving phase $= \dfrac{V}{A_m}$ (3)

From (1), (2) and (3)

$$R_f = \left[\frac{V}{A_m + \alpha A_s}\right] \div \frac{V}{A_m}$$

$$= \frac{A_m}{A_m + \alpha A_s}$$

$$\therefore R_f(A_m + \alpha A_s) = A_m$$

$$\therefore R_f \alpha A_s = A_m(1 - R_f)$$

$$\therefore \alpha = \left[\frac{A_m(1 - R_f)}{A_s R_f}\right] \qquad (4)$$

There is therefore a unique relationship between the R_f value and the distribution coefficient α, defined in terms of concentration for any given ratio of A_m to A_s which depends on the closeness of packing of the column.

It is possible to eliminate the area of cross-section terms from equation (4) by defining a distribution coefficient f on a slightly different basis from α.

$$f = \frac{\left[\begin{array}{c}\text{weight of substance associated with stationary phase in}\\ \text{equilibrium with unit volume of moving phase}\end{array}\right]}{\text{weight of substance per unit volume of moving phase}}$$

$$= \frac{\left[\begin{array}{c}\text{weight of substance associated with unit volume of}\\ \text{stationary phase}\end{array}\right] \times \dfrac{A_s}{A_m}}{\text{weight of substance per unit volume of moving phase}}$$

$$= \frac{A_s \alpha}{A_m} \qquad (5)$$

From (4) and (5) $\quad f = \dfrac{1 - R_f}{R_f}$ (6)

f can also represent the proportionality factor in the adsorption isotherms and it is proportional to the surface area of the solid phase in adsorption chromatography.

Equations corresponding to (4) and (6) have been worked out in connection with theories of partition, ion-exchange and adsorption chromatography respectively by Martin and Synge (1941), Mayer and Tompkins (1947), and Le Rosen *et al.* (1951).

Calculation of corresponding values of f and R_f from equation (6) shows that workable values of R_f are obtained for a wide range of values of f (Table 2.3).

TABLE 2.3. CORRESPONDING VALUES OF f AND R_f

f (α when $A_s = A_m$)	R_f
99	0·01
19	0·05
9	0·1
4	0·2
2	0·33
1	0·5
0·5	0·67
0·25	0·8

Theory of the Chromtaogram Based upon 'Theoretical Plates.' Martin and Synge (1941) were the first to work out a satisfactory theory for the behaviour of substances on chromatographic columns. It gave a quantitative picture of the variation in the concentration of solute at different positions and times, as well as showing how resolution depends upon column length. Although the theory was formulated specifically for liquid–liquid (partition) chromatograms, it has considerably wider application and its importance and usefulness justify a brief mention here.

By analogy with the processes occurring in packed fractional-distillation columns, the chromatographic column was considered to consist of a large number of thin, horizontal, *theoretical plates* within each of which equilibrium of the two phases was assumed to occur. Even where equilibrium is not quite reached at any point, the concept is still valid if the solution issuing from each theoretical plate would be in equilibrium with the mean concentration of solute in the stationary phase inside the plate. The height equivalent of one theoretical plate (h.e.t.p.) is the thickness of a layer of the column for which this condition holds. In chromatography the h.e.t.p. may be assumed to be constant throughout the column without serious error.

Martin and Synge made two further assumptions: (i) that diffusion of the solute from one plate to the next was negligible, and, (ii) that the distribution ratio α of the solute between the phases was independent of both the concentration of solute and the presence of other solutes. This assumption regarding solute concentration is valid for most partition systems except for high concentrations. It also justifies application of the theory to other systems which have linear distribution isotherms.

If the above assumptions were made, it was demonstrated that when unit mass of solute is placed in the first plate of a chromatogram, which is then developed with volume v of pure solvent, the quantity in the $(r + 1)$th plate (numbered in sequence) is given by the equation

$$Q_{r+1} = \frac{1}{\sqrt{(2\pi r)}}\left(\frac{v}{rV}\right)^{r} \mathrm{e}^{r-v/V} \tag{7}$$

where $V = h\,(A_m + \alpha A_s)$; h is the h.e.t.p.; and A_m, A_s and α have the significance given on page 34.

The maximum concentration of solute near the centre of a moving zone was shown to occupy the $(r + 1)$th plate when

$$v = rV \tag{8}$$

being given by the equation

$$Q_{r+1} = \frac{1}{\sqrt{(2\pi r)}} \tag{9}$$

deduced from (7) and (8). The distance of this point from the top of the column is

$$\frac{v}{A_m + \alpha A_s}$$

By plotting the concentration of solute in the $(r + 1)$th plate against v/V, making use of equation (7), a curve of the type shown in Fig. 2.12 is obtained. As r, the number of theoretical plates, approaches infinity the curve approaches the normal curve of error to which it approximates closely when $r > 100$.

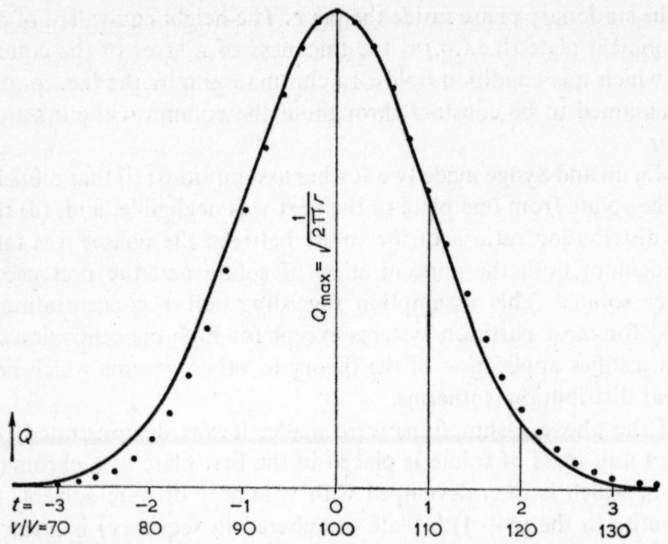

FIG. 2.12. Quantities of a migrating substance in successive theoretical plates of a chromatogram.

The points represent the relation between Q and v/V for $r = 100$ in Martin and Synge's general equation (7). The full line is the normal curve of error with abscissa t, i.e. $Q/Q_{max} = \exp[-\frac{1}{2}t^2]$ (Martin and Synge, *Biochem. J.* 35, 1361.)

The ordinates of the curve can then be expressed according to the normal curve of error by the equation

$$\frac{v}{V} = r + t\sqrt{r} + \frac{t^2}{3} \qquad (10)$$

where t is the abscissa of the error curve shown in Fig. 2.12. Unit value of t represents the standard deviation. The area under the curve is given by

$$\frac{v}{V} = r + t\sqrt{r} + \frac{t^2}{4} \qquad (11)$$

When $t = 3$ the area under the tail of the curve is only 0·13 per cent of the whole area. This shows that two peaks may be regarded as completely separated for practical purposes when their point of greatest overlap is separated from each summit by values of v/V equivalent to a value of 3 for t in the standard curve of error. It is possible to calculate from equation (11) the length of a column (in terms of the number of theoretical plates) to give any required degree of separation of two substances whose distribution coefficients are known.

In practice it cannot be assumed that the whole of a substance is present, simultaneously, in the first theoretical plate. It is bound to occupy a number of plates and the peak is broadened correspondingly. Increased resolution for a column of given length may be obtained by reducing the h.e.t.p. This in turn is achieved by using a smaller particle size for the stationary phase or reducing the flow rate so that an equilibrium state is more nearly approached. There is a limit below which reduction of flow rate is disadvantageous since diffusion of the solute more than offsets the advantages of the near-equilibrium state by decreasing the sharpness of the peaks.

The distribution coefficient usually varies somewhat over a wide range of concentration and gives rise to the *tailing* effect described on page 26. This steepens the leading edges of the peaks and flattens the trailing part. Interaction between neighbouring substances may also occur as described under displacement methods. It is seldom marked under *elution* conditions but occurs where columns are very heavily loaded in relation to their capacity. This displacement effect makes the peaks sharper than they would be otherwise.

The theory of Martin and Synge first clearly described the manner in which a substance migrates through a chromatogram under the influence of the moving phase. Except when other migrating substances are present in high concentrations, as in displacement chromatography, the zone occupied by a migrating material is not characterized by almost vertical edges and a flat top (Fig. 2.11). The more usual form is a peak with sigmoid leading and trailing edges on either side of a sharp maximum, closely resembling the curve of error (Fig. 2.12).

The theory shows how, during the passage of such a peak through a column, the concentration at the maximum must decrease as r increases, equation (9), and the peak becomes progressively broader and less steep-sided. It is important to notice that this broadening and flattening is an essential feature of the chromatographic process resulting from continual interchange of the migrating substance between the moving and stationary phases and will occur even when no significant diffusion of the substance in the moving phase takes place. The theory also accounts for the decrease in height and increase in width of peaks representing successive zones of different substances, present in equivalent quantities, when they reach a given point in the chromatographic system. This effect is clearly seen in experimental elution diagrams of amino acids from ion-exchange resin columns (Fig. 6.3).

Uses of Chromatography

As a separative method of the widest available scope, chromatography is applicable to the whole range of gaseous, volatile and soluble substances, from light elementary gases to proteins having a molecular weight of several millions. It can be used as an analytical tool for exploratory purposes to decide how many components are contained in a mixture, for qualitative studies in which the individual substances are each identified, or for quantitative determinations of each component of a mixture. The analytical uses of chromatography are not limited to preliminary separations to be followed by standard methods of analysis, since the chromatographic characteristics obtained during the course of separation (e.g. sequence of elution, R_f values) usually provide valuable evidence concerning identity.

Chromatography is also useful as a preparative method for obtaining substances in a high state of purity. It is usually possible to remove even those impurities whose properties most resemble those of the substance in question by choosing a suitable system and a column of sufficient length. At the same time, it is a simple matter to obtain information about the amounts and types of impurities present.

Chromatographic processes may be scaled down to practically any required degree, the limits usually being set by the ancillary methods required for the detection of the separated substances. The technique is therefore useful both for micro-analysis and for separating minute amounts of rare substances for subsequent investigation of their properties. Applied thus, chromatography has found extensive use in the separation of rare earth and transuranic elements.

For preparative work in many fields of research, chromatography may be scaled-up, without undue loss of efficiency, by the use of wider columns, although problems due to irregular fronts may arise as the column diameter is increased. On the other hand, chromatography has not as yet found extensive use on an industrial scale. Because the amounts of both stationary and moving phases are large compared with the quantity of material separated, the plant needed is both bulky and expensive in comparison with its output. Furthermore, in its most usual form, chromatography is a batch process rather than a continuous one, which would be more acceptable for commercial use.

The Literature of Chromatography

During the last thirty years, chromatography has developed into a highly efficient technique, and an enormous expansion in the number of its applications has taken place. For this reason, much of the original literature containing descriptions of useful methods is scattered throughout a selection of journals dealing with physics, chemistry, biology and medicine as well as specialities so diverse as agriculture and nuclear physics. Biochemistry has been a particularly fruitful field for the development and application of chromatographic methods and many valuable papers are to be found in the *Biochemical Journal* and the *Journal of Biological Chemistry*. Short communications in *Nature* frequently contain accounts of new or modified techniques.

Reviews on the progress of chromatography have appeared in *Analytical Chemistry* for the even numbered years beginning with 1950. The second edition of the text-book on *Chromatography* by Lederer and Lederer (1957) contains nearly four thousand references, covering original papers up to the end of 1955. In 1958, the *Journal of Chromatography* was established; besides original papers in English, French and German, dealing primarily with chromatography, it includes a supplement of R_f values, research reports, notes and reviews. These reviews are also published annually, translated into English, as *Reviews of Chromatography*.

The preceding paragraphs indicate that a book of the size of the present volume cannot hope to be a detailed reference source to the whole of the past literature on chromatography. The sources already quoted should, however, permit the reader to trace any information required. For the same reason it is impossible to include details of all the very large numbers of published chromatographic methods. Only those considered to be especially useful and typical will be mentioned, together with the necessary background of information which is most likely to be required in investigations involving practical chromatography.

REFERENCES

Claesson, S. (1947). *Arkiv Kemi Mineral. Geol.* **24A,** No. 16.
Drake, B. (1949). *Analyt. chim. Acta* **3,** 452.
Gordon, A. H., Martin, A. J. P. and Synge, R. L. M. (1944). *Biochem. J.* **38,** 65.
Hagdahl, L. (1948). *Acta chem. Scand.* **2,** 574.
Hagdahl, L. (1954). *Science Tools* **1,** 21.
Lathe, G. H. and Ruthven, C. R. J. (1956). *Biochem. J.* **62,** 665.
Lederer, E. and Lederer, M. (1957). *Chromatography—A Review of Principles and Applications*, 2nd edn., Elsevier, Amsterdam.
Le Rosen, A. L., Monaghan, C. A., Rivet, C. A. and Smith, E. D. (1951). *Proc. Louisiana Acad. Sci.* **12,** 99.
Martin, A. J. P. and Synge, R. L. M. (1941). *Biochem. J.* **35,** 1358.
Mayer, S. W. and Tompkins, E. R. (1947). *J. Amer. chem. Soc.* **69,** 2866.
Partridge, S. M. and Brimley, R. C. (1951). *Biochem. J.* **48,** 313.
Reichstein, T. and van Euw, J. (1938). *Helv. Chim. Acta* **21,** 1197.
Samuelson, O. (1952). *Ion Exchangers in Analytical Chemistry.* Almqvits and Wiksell Boktr. AB, Stockholm.
Strain, H. H. (1960). *Analyt. Chem.* **32,** 3R.
Tiselius, A. (1940). *Arkiv Kemi Mineral. Geol.* **14B,** No. 22.
Tiselius, A. (1943). *Kolloid-Z.* **105,** 101.

CHAPTER 3

APPARATUS

APPARATUS FOR COLUMN CHROMATOGRAPHY

Columns

The tubes into which chromatographic columns are packed are normally made of glass, which allows observation of the settling of the stationary phase and the level of the liquid as well as inspection for air bubbles in the column. In addition, it is sometimes useful to observe the movement of bands of coloured substances down the column. Borosilicate-glass tubing of moderate thickness probably offers the best combination of properties as regards resistance to chemical reagents, and to mechanical and thermal shock.

The effective length of the column may vary considerably. Columns ranging from 2–150 cm are in routine laboratory use. The minimum internal diameter which permits packing the column by ordinary methods is approximately 4 mm. There is no definite upper limit to the diameter, which is mainly dictated by convenience and the amount of material to be separated. Straightness is particularly important in long, narrow columns since it permits even deposition of the column material when the particles settle under gravity.

Various methods for supporting the stationary phase have been suggested. Early methods included glass-wool plugs, filter paper and sand resting on perforated porcelain plates. For most purposes, however, sintered-glass disks are most efficient, since they form an integral part of the column and do not introduce a different type of material (Fig. 3.1). Perhaps the most difficult operation in the construction of glass columns, is to fuse these sintered disks in position in a satisfactory manner, especially for the smaller sizes, 1 cm or less in diameter. If insufficient heat is applied, the sinter does not fuse with the tube all round, so that particles of the stationary phase may escape between the disk and the tube. On the other hand, if the tube is heated too strongly, the sinter may fuse together into a solid impermeable mass. Skill is required to regulate the application of the flame between these extremes. The smallest size of sintered disk available commercially is 1 cm in diameter. When smaller disks are required, the size may be reduced by careful use of a carborundum grinding wheel. It is also possible to form sinters *in situ* from glass powder. Sintered disks of porosity 2 (average pore diameter 40–60 μ) are sufficiently fine completely to hold most types of stationary phase, while for the coarser materials, porosity 1 (100–120 μ), is satisfactory and permits faster flow rates. If blocking of the sinter by particles of solid tends to occur, the trouble may be overcome by placing a disk of filter paper over the sinter before packing the column. Sintered disks are liable to disintegrate on prolonged contact with strong alkalis even in dilute solution.

It is sometimes useful to have a tap fitted below the sintered disk so that flow through the column may be stopped when required. Columns with standard, conical, ground joints are available with such a tap fitted as a detachable unit (Fig. 3.2), while in the larger diameters the sintered disk also is available in a detachable unit (Fig. 3.3). The separate parts are held firmly together by tension springs fitted over projecting glass hooks. If the lower end of the column is cut off at 45° and the tip drawn out and fused to a small blob of glass, the eluant will drip from this point or run smoothly into a vessel placed in contact with the glass blob, while the portion of the tube below the sintered disk remains empty. This reduces the possibility of remixing of separated substances.

A standard ground-glass socket at the top of the column is useful for connecting the reservoir which contains the moving phase. It is important to ensure that no particles of the stationary phase remain on this ground surface as they might cause leakage. Standard joint columns are normally available with internal diameters of 10, 18, 38 and 48 mm, and with effective lengths from 10–90 cm.

Columns for Special Purposes. Tapered tubes which facilitate the extrusion of the column for tests with streak reagents have been described by Georges *et al.* (1946). Gault and Ronez (1950) used tubes constructed in sections with interchangeable joints so that the column could be opened at different heights. The Tiselius–Claesson columns for frontal analysis were made in the form of rectangular cells from plastics, glass or metal.

Hagdahl (1954) designed a standard series of coupled columns which could be fitted together one below the other to form a composite column (Fig. 4.4), in order to overcome loss of resolution due to irregular and blurred fronts which may arise when high concentrations of substances are separated in single columns (page 25).

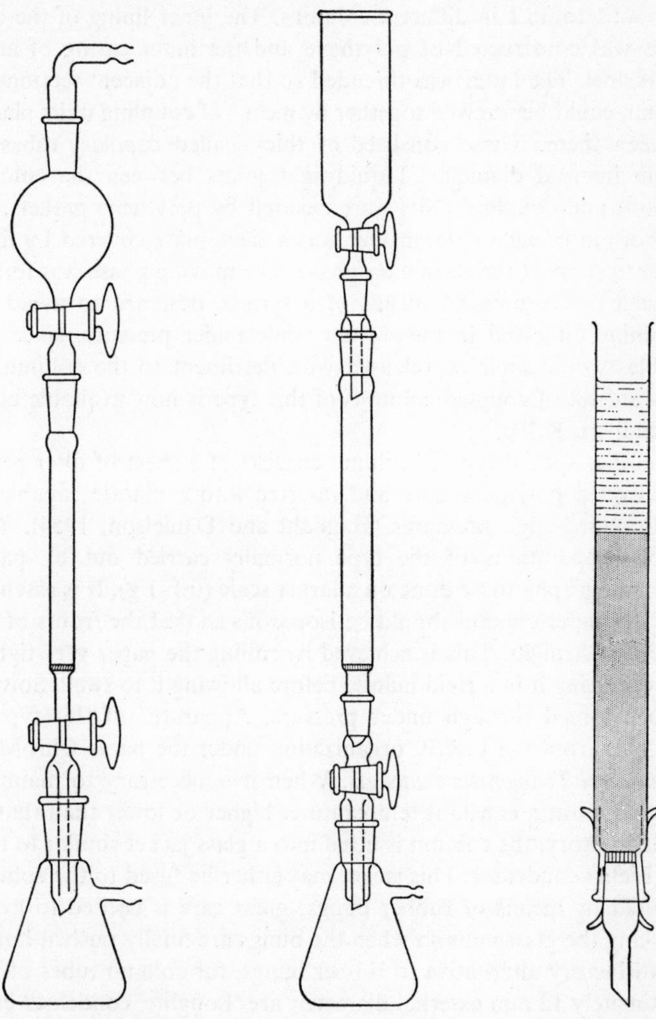

FIG. 3.1. Apparatus for column chromatography with fused tap, sintered disk and ground joints.

Fig. 3.2. Column fitted with detachable tap.

FIG. 3.3. Column with detachable sintered disk.

A 2 : 1 volume ratio between successive columns was chosen as being most generally useful, and the standard series had six columns of capacity 16, 8, 4, 2, 1 and 0·5 ml, although normally only three or four are used at any one time. The length to diameter ratio varied from 4 : 1 to 6 : 1 in different columns. The inner lining of the columns was constructed of polythene and the outer casing of acid-proof steel. The latter was threaded so that the adjacent sections of column could be screwed together by means of coupling units placed between them. These consisted of thick-walled capillary tubes of 1 mm internal diameter. Liquid-tight joints between the column sections and coupling units were ensured by polythene gaskets. At the bottom of each column unit was a sieve plate covered by filter paper to support the stationary phase. The moving phase was forced through the column by means of a syringe designed to avoid air becoming dissolved in the solvent while under pressure, since gas bubbles would later be released with detriment to the column. A standard set of coupled columns of this type is now available commercially (L.K.B).

Another special type of column consists of a sheet of filter paper rolled on a polythene core and inserted into a mantle capable of withstanding high pressures (Hagdahl and Danielson, 1954). This enables separations of the type normally carried out by paper chromatography to be done on a larger scale (0·1–1 g). It is essential that the paper column should be isoporous so that the fronts of the zones are straight. This is achieved by rolling the paper very tightly and enclosing it in a rigid mantle before allowing it to swell. Solvent is then forced through under pressure. Apparatus of this type is available from the L.K.B. organization under the name ChroMax.

Constant Temperature Jackets. When it is necessary to maintain the column at a constant temperature, higher or lower than that of the laboratory, the column is fitted into a glass jacket similar to that of a Liebig condenser. This jacket may either be fused to the column or fitted by means of rubber bungs; great care is needed to avoid breaking the glass column when the bungs are finally pushed home. A satisfactory alternative to rubber bungs, for column tubes of approximately 12 mm external diameter, are 'Longlife' condenser ends (J. W. Towers, Ltd.) made of rubber with metal inlet and outlet tubes.

Heating the jacket by the vapour of a liquid which boils at a suitable temperature has been suggested. It is more convenient, however, to circulate hot water from a constant-temperature bath through the jacket. For many purposes a temperature control within $\pm 1\,^{\circ}\mathrm{C}$ is sufficient and an adequate system can easily be made from a saucepan of 10-l. capacity, fitted with a 750-W electric-kettle element and a Sunvic TS 2 thermostat projecting downwards through the lid (Fig. 3.4). A hot-wire relay (e.g. Type F 102/4) is wired between the

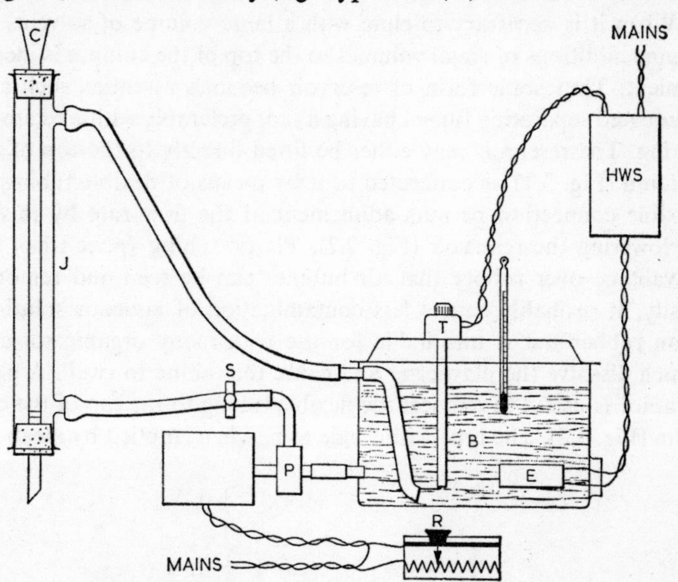

FIG. 3.4. Constant-temperature bath and circulating system for column jackets.

B	Constant-temperature bath.	P	Centrifugal pump.
C	Column.	R	Variable resistance.
E	Kettle element.	S	Screw clip.
HWS	Hot-wire switch.	T	Thermostat.
J	Column jacket.		

thermostat and the heater to protect the thermostat contacts from the repeated arcing due to the large current required by the heater. The water is pumped through the jacket of the column by an electric centrifugal pump (e.g. Stuart Turner No. 10) the speed of which can be controlled by a variable series resistance. In view of the characteristics of the centrifugal pump, it is advisable partially to restrict the flow by means of a screw clip on the rubber tubing on the outlet side, unless the water has to be pumped up more than about 4 ft; this avoids overloading the pump motor. Rubber tubing should be of medium wall thickness to avoid kinking and all joints should be wired (20 s.w.g. copper) to prevent them from working loose. The commutator of the pump motor should be cleaned with fine glass paper after each three days' continuous running.

Supply of Solvent

When it is necessary to elute with a large volume of solvent, repeated additions of small volumes to the top of the column is inconvenient. Thus some form of reservoir becomes essential, such as a graduated separating funnel having a tap, preferably with a retaining spring. The reservoir may either be fitted directly to the top of the column (Fig. 3.1) or connected to it by means of flexible tubing. A flexible connection permits adjustment of the flow rate by raising or lowering the reservoir (Fig. 2.2). Plastic tubing (p.v.c.) has the advantage over rubber that air bubbles can be seen and removed easily. It probably causes less contamination of aqueous solutions than rubber but is unsuitable for use with many organic solvents which dissolve the plasticizer and cause the tubing to swell. A glass adaptor is useful to connect the flexible tubing to the top of the column (Fig. 3.5). The type with a side arm, when emptied by means of

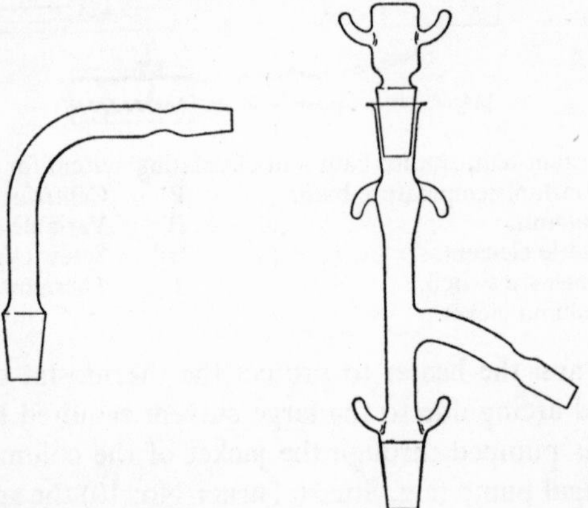

FIG. 3.5. Adaptors for connecting flexible tubing to top of columns. The glass hooks enable the adaptor to be held in place by springs.

a Pasteur pipette, permits the solvent to be changed at any time without danger of spilling down the outside of the column.

With organic solvents it is preferable to connect the reservoir directly to the top of the column and to regulate the flow by means of a separate device (Fig. 3.6), which can either increase or reduce the pressure. Constant positive pressure may be applied by means of a nitrogen cylinder or some form of pump (e.g. an aquarium aerator), controlled to give a constant pressure by means of a Marriot bottle (see also Fig. 3.7). An apparatus for pressures up to 120 lb/in^2 is described by Mowery (1951). Even where only small liquid heads are used, different parts of the apparatus should be held together by springs or rubber bands fitted over glass hooks. For high pressures, strong springs or clamps are essential. With volatile solvents, it is better to apply pressure to the top of the column, than vacuum to the receiver, because of the danger of bubble formation.

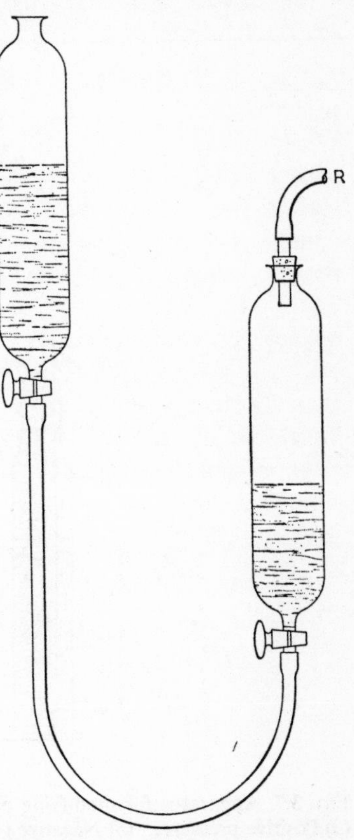

FIG. 3.6. Pressurizing device for columns.
Flexible tubing at R is connected to top of solvent reservoir.

For gradient-elution systems continuous mixture of two or more liquids is required, so that elution is brought about by a solvent mixture which is continuously changing in composition. The mixing is carried out in a vessel which takes the place of the usual reservoir. This vessel is always fitted with a stirrer and in one form of the apparatus is connected by narrow-bore tubing to another vessel which contains the second solvent. As liquid leaves the mixing chamber this solvent gradually enters and changes the composition of the liquid flowing into the column. Magnetic stirrers are most suitable for this application since they do not require direct connection from outside to inside the mixing vessel. The reservoir vessels may be connected together in different ways giving gradients with various characteristics. Further variation of the type of gradient

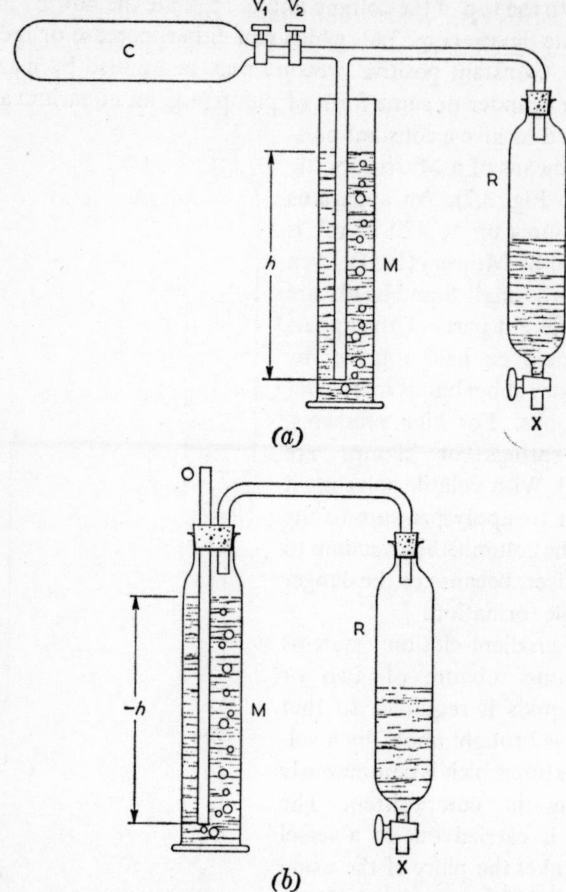

FIG. 3.7. Apparatus for modifying pressure applied to column.
(*a*) Positive pressure. (*b*) Negative pressure.

C Cylinder of gas or compressor.
V_1 V_2 Pressure reducing valves.
M Marriot bottle containing water or mercury.
R Solvent reservoir.
X Connection to top of column.
O Open to atmosphere.

The additional pressure (or suction) applied to the solvent supplying the column is proportional to distance *h*, which can be adjusted.

is possible by changing the relative sizes and shapes of the vessels (Fig. 3.8).

Pumps. Recently-developed methods of automatic quantitative analysis, based upon column chromatography, require the continuous pumping of liquids at slow but constant and known rates. If a liquid is pumped through a column at a fixed rate, and the column effluent is mixed with a reagent pumped by a second constant-speed pump,

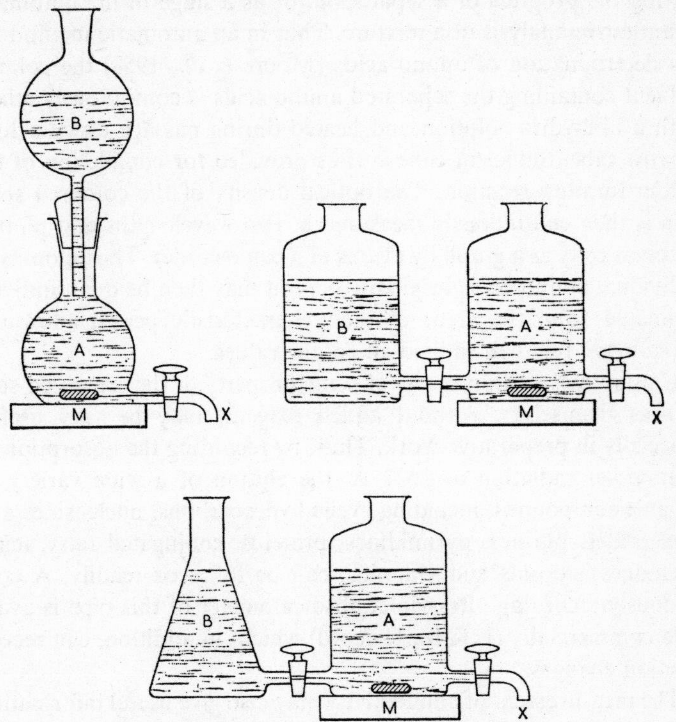

FIG. 3.8. Apparatus for mixing solvents in gradient elution.
A First solvent. M Magnetic stirrer.
B Second solvent. X Connection to column.

the proportions of effluent and reagent in the mixture and its rate of flow will both be constant. A commercially available (L.K.B.) pump of this type has two glass syringes operated reciprocally by a low-power synchronous motor. This provides a continuous constant-velocity flow, without pulses, which may be varied in steps from 3–50 ml/h. The liquid only comes into contact with glass in this apparatus. Other types of pump, which operate by the action of either a roller or mechanical fingers across plastic tubing containing the liquid being pumped, may also have applications in chromatography.

Apparatus for Continuous Measurements on the Column Effluent

Continuous measurement of some property of the solution emerging from the column may be done either as a useful means of following the progress of a separation, or as a stage in the automatic quantitative analysis of a mixture. Thus in an automatic method for the determination of amino acids (Moore *et al.*, 1958) the column effluent containing the separated amino acids is continuously mixed with a ninhydrin solution and heated during passage down a long narrow tube. Sufficient time is thus provided for completion of the colour-forming reaction. The optical density of the coloured solution is then continuously measured at two wavelengths and plotted automatically as a graph by means of a pen recorder. The amounts of individual amino acids originally present may then be quantitatively estimated from the areas of their characteristic peaks, allowance being made for their individual colour values.

Continuous measurements of some property of the separated substances themselves, without added reagent, may be very useful, especially in preparative work. Thus, by recording the absorption of ultra-violet radiation at 2537 Å, the elution of a wide variety of organic compounds, including cyclic hydrocarbons, nucleosides and nucleotides, purines, pyrimidines, proteins, conjugated fatty acids, hormones, steroids and vitamins, can be followed readily. A continuously-recording ultra-violet absorptiometer of this type is available commercially (L.K.B., Uvicord) which, in addition, can record fraction changes.

The measurement of conductivity may also give useful information concerning the changes in composition of some types of effluent. James *et al*. (1951) gave details for the construction of a continuous-conductivity recorder for use with columns. Another instrument (L.K.B., Conductolyser) is available which can measure cell resistances in three ranges up to 10,000 Ω, using an a.c. bridge circuit working at 2000 c/s. The instrument is adjusted initially for the minimum conductivity of the solvent alone and then plots changes of conductivity on a recorder.

Miscellaneous Apparatus

Chromatography, in its various aspects, requires most of the ordinary apparatus of the chemical laboratory. For the addition of accurately known small volumes of the solution of the mixture to be separated to columns, pipettes with their tips bent at right angles and calibrated by blowing out the jet are very useful. For volumes less than 1 ml, automatic zero, high-precision micro-pipettes (H. J. Elliott, Ltd.) are particularly convenient.

A spectrophotometer which can be fitted with microcells, a fluorimeter and a semi-micro balance are also valuable for chromatographic work.

Fraction Collectors

It is often useful to collect separately, successive portions (or fractions) of the effluent from a column, in order to follow the progress of an experiment in which several substances are eluted. For short runs the change of collecting vessel can be made manually, but this becomes inconvenient even when the elution lasts for only a few hours. An automatic *fraction collector* (or *fraction cutter*) enables an experiment of this sort, lasting several days, to be carried out, if necessary in the absence of the investigator. Usually the fractions are required to be of equal volume within more or less narrow limits according to the purpose of the investigation. To achieve this, two basic types of fraction collector have been developed which differ in their mode of operation.

1. *Time-operated* fraction collectors change the collecting vessel after the lapse of equal intervals of time, which can usually be selected within the range of the instrument. If the rate of effluent flow is constant, successive fractions are equal in volume and, by adjustment of the timer, this volume may be brought to the required value. In practice it is difficult to maintain an absolutely constant flow rate in a column running under gravity, and variations of flow will be reflected in unequal fraction volumes. This effect may be reduced by fitting a constant-pressure device to the reservoir above the column or eliminated by forcing the liquid through the column by a constant rate pump. Where fractions of closely similar volume are essential, it is usually more convenient to have some form of flow-operated collector. A further disadvantage of the time-operated type is that, with some designs, occasional drops of effluent may escape collection during the change over. The main advantage of this type is simplicity in construction, since all that is required is a release mechanism operated by a timer.

2. *Flow-operated* collectors are designed to collect fractions of constant size independently of the rate of effluent flow. A fraction collector of this type is like a clock, the rate of which is controlled by the flow of liquid out of the column. There are three main subdivisions of this form of apparatus which differ in the method of flow measurement.

a. *Gravimetric* instruments collect fractions of equal weight by having the collecting vessel either hanging from, or standing on, a platform which is attached to one arm of a balance. When sufficient solvent has collected, the balance tips and moves an empty collecting vessel into position on the platform. It is essential that all the empty collecting vessels should be of exactly equal weight and that the balance arm and associated mechanism should not show any tendency to stick.

b. *Volumetric* fraction collectors operate by direct measurement of the volume of liquid collected. Several types have been developed.

(i) intermediate vessel with *siphon*,
(ii) intermediate vessel with one or two *valves*,
(iii) graduated collecting vessels.

The *siphon vessel* is interposed between the bottom of the column and the collecting vessels. It fills gradually from the column and then siphons-over rapidly into the awaiting test tube. Sometimes the siphon is attached to a balance arm, which operates the changeover mechanism but does not affect the volume measurement. The lower limit of fraction size is approximately 2 ml. The accuracy of the volume measurements, particularly for the smaller volumes, depends critically on the design and the quality of workmanship of the glass siphon, since it is essential that premature as well as incomplete siphoning are both avoided. A separate siphon is required for each size of fraction which has to be collected. *Valve-operated* intermediate vessels are usually adjustable for a range of volumes (Fig. 3.9). Normally the outlet valve is closed so that the effluent rises until the meniscus operates a photoelectric or conductivity relay, which then opens the valve, allowing the liquid to drain into the collecting vessel below. When sufficient time has elapsed for complete drainage, the outlet valve is closed and an empty collecting vessel is brought into position. Fraction collectors with *graduated flasks* as collecting vessels have been used, where great accuracy is necessary in the volume measurement. The level of each individual flask is previously adjusted so that the meniscus operates a photoelectric relay as it crosses the graduation mark.

c. *Drop-counting* fraction collectors are especially suitable for measuring very small fractions down to approximately 0·1 ml, whereas the types already described have a lower limit at about 1 ml. For fractions to be of constant volume, the surface tension of the effluent must remain constant, since this in turn influences the drop and fraction sizes. Variation in the surface tension of aqueous solutions may be minimized by adding a detergent.

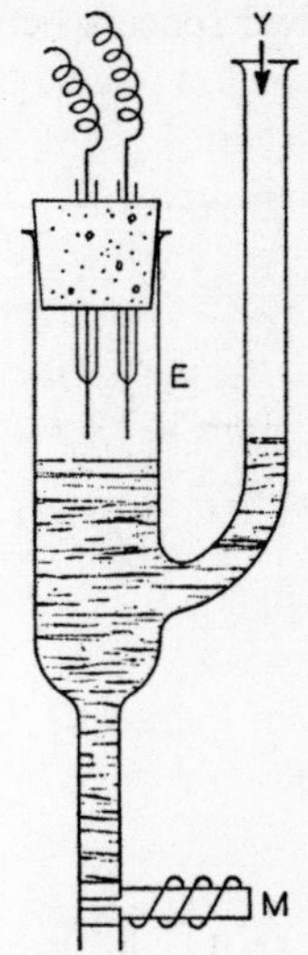

FIG. 3.9. Intermediate vessel for fraction collector, operated by conductivity relay and magnetic valve.
E Platinum electrodes (adjustable for height).
M Magnetic valve.
Y Inlet for column effluent.

The column effluent should run smoothly into a funnel having a jet of the required diameter, where a drop forms and eventually falls directly into the collecting vessel. As the drop detaches itself from the jet, it either momentarily interrupts a photoelectric relay or makes contact between two wires (Fig. 3.10). The resulting signal operates a counter, which may be either electromagnetic (e.g. uni-selector switch), electronic or driven by an electric motor. The counter can be set for any number of drops within a wide range and when that number has fallen, it provides an impulse for the fraction collector to change over and then resets itself to count the next fraction.

Variation of fraction size with change of temperature or solvent composition must be considered as a possible limitation of the accuracy of the drop-counting method for any particular application. The method is unsuitable for use with very volatile solvents especially where the rate of drop formation is very slow.

Turntables. It is possible to design a fraction collector for any form of collecting vessel, but test tubes are nearly always used for fractions up to about 50 ml. Their compact shape enables a large number to be arranged in a limited area, while the parallel sides simplify the method of location. The usual arrangement for bringing successive tubes into position beneath the column is a circular rack or turntable (Fig. 3.11). This has holes for the tubes which are of a size permitting accurate location with ease of insertion and withdrawal. The most convenient form of turntable has three circular disks with rigid spacers between them. The upper and centre disks have holes

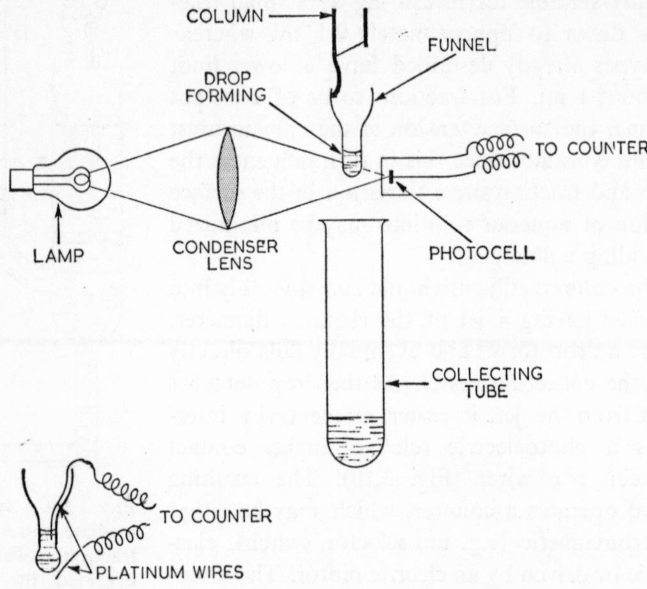

FIG. 3.10. Formation and counting of drops by photoelectric and conductivity relays.

in corresponding positions, while the tubes rest on the lowest disk, which is not perforated. This ensures that they are positively located and upright [Fig. 3.12(*a*)].

In the simplest design, tubes are arranged in a circle near the periphery of the turntable [Fig. 3.12(*b*)]. The capacity is limited to perhaps 100 tubes for a 30-in. diameter turntable. To increase the capacity of the turntable the holes may be arranged in a spiral [Fig. 3.12(*c*)]. With this design, in addition to the normal stepwise rotation of the turntable, its centre must gradually move towards or away from the collecting point. For this purpose the central axis is mounted on a pivoted arm. Another arrangement used in some commercial fraction collectors, consists of two or more concentric circles of holes. Each circle has the same number of holes, corresponding ones in different rows being placed exactly on the same radius. The turntable revolves in steps until it reaches a predetermined point X

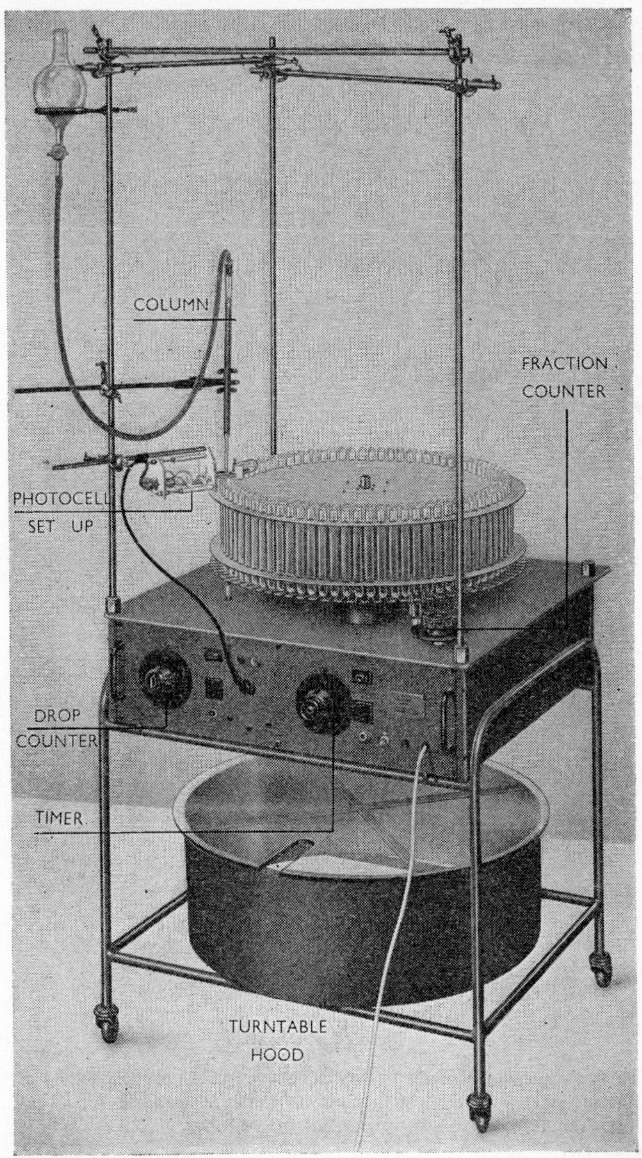

FIG. 3.11. Fraction collector with alternative photoelectric drop counting and time-operated mechanisms (*The Locarte Company*).

or Y, when it moves across to bring a tube in the next circle into position [Fig. 3.12(*d*)]. In another design [Fig. 3.12(*e*)] with a similar

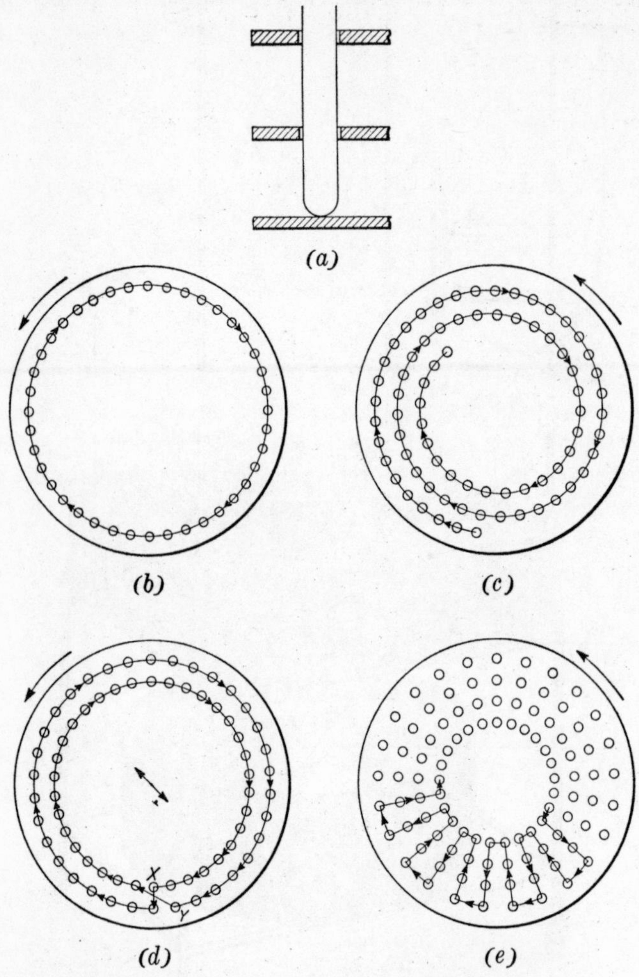

FIG. 3.12. Arrangement of holes in turntables for fraction collectors.
(*a*) Method of supporting test tubes in turntable (elevation).
(*b*)—(*e*) Plan views of various arrangements of tubes.
(*b*) Circular.
(*c*) Spiral.
(*d*) Concentric circles with automatic traverse at points X and Y.
(*e*) Square-wave collection.
Arrows outside circles show direction of rotation of turntables. Arrows inside circles show the order in which fractions are delivered into test tubes.

pattern of holes, the turntable moves radially from one hole to the next until the inner or outer row is reached, when it rotates to the next position in the same circle. The turntable then moves radially in the opposite direction to that taken previously. The tubes are thus filled in a 'square-wave' pattern. This design has been used in a commercially manufactured fraction collector in which the turntable is built up from several detachable test tube racks.

In another commercial fraction collector, the turntable is replaced by a flexible belt of tubes, joined together by stainless-steel clips. The train of tubes is wound in a stepwise manner from one turret, past the collecting point, to a second turret. When the fractions have been collected, the belt may be dismantled into self-supporting sections of convenient length.

When fractions of large volume are collected, it becomes unwieldy to support the necessarily large containers on a turntable. A better design is to arrange the vessels in fixed positions round a circle having the column in its centre. A radial glass tube, mounted on a central rotating platform, transfers the effluent from the column to the containers and moves round from one vessel to the next as each fraction is collected.

Drives and Locating Devices. At the conclusion of the collection of

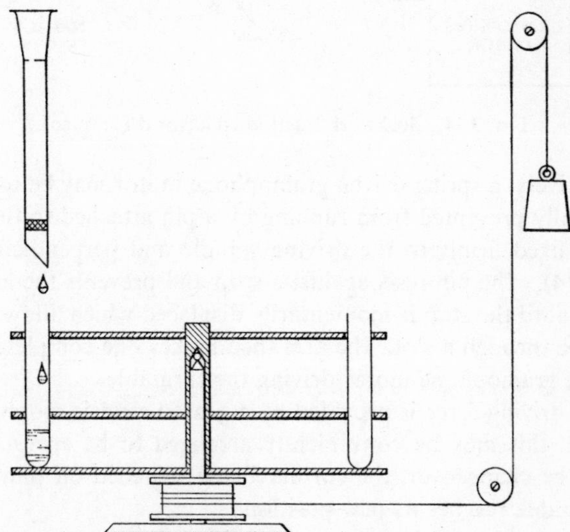

FIG. 3.13. Weight-driven fraction collector (elevation).

a particular fraction, the next empty tube must be brought into position to receive its fraction in turn. To achieve this, a mechanical drive is required to move the turntable, and in addition some kind of locating device to stop it in exactly the right position with the centre of the new test tube beneath the collecting point. No cumulative error of positioning is permissible since eventually the space between adjacent tubes would arrive under the collecting point and the solution would be lost.

A reliable continuous driving force (Fig. 3.13) for use in conjunction with an escapement, is provided by a heavy weight attached to a cord which is wrapped round a drum, firmly fixed to the turntable.

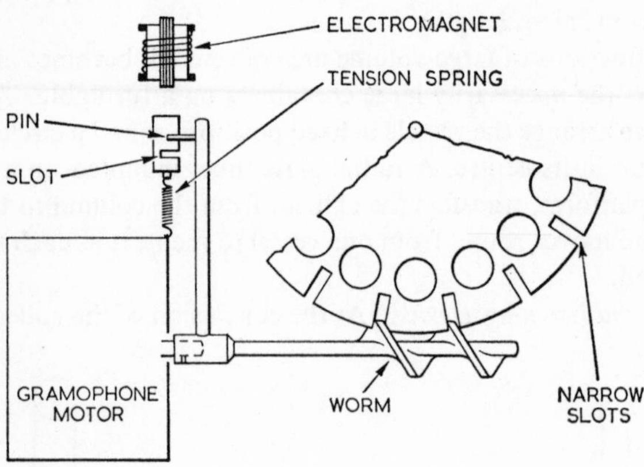

FIG. 3.14. Clockwork fraction collector drive (plan).

Alternatively, a spring-driven gramophone motor may be used. This is normally prevented from running by a pin attached to the end of an arm fixed firmly to the driving spindle and perpendicular to it (Fig. 3.14). The pin rests against a stop and prevents the arm from turning until the stop is momentarily displaced which allows the pin to escape through a slot. The arm then makes one complete revolution, the gramophone motor driving the turntable.

If the driving force is provided by a geared electric motor or by a solenoid, this may be conveniently arranged to be energized only during the changeover, the current being switched off immediately the turntable reaches its new position.

The turntable may be driven round through a gear, making use of slots cut at regular intervals in the outer edge of one of the turntable disks. Narrow slots, spaced alternately between the test-tube holes, may be engaged by a worm, cut and bent from sheet brass, so that its pitch is equal to the distance between successive slots (Fig. 3.14). With somewhat wider slots (6–8 mm), the form of drive shown in Fig. 3.15 may be used. Two smooth pegs attached to a small wheel, which turns through half a revolution at each fraction change, engage in adjacent slots in the turntable. This type of drive has the advantage that power is applied slowly, the turntable reaching maximum speed at the halfway position, being brought to rest again slowly. Small errors in the angular positioning of the wheel carrying

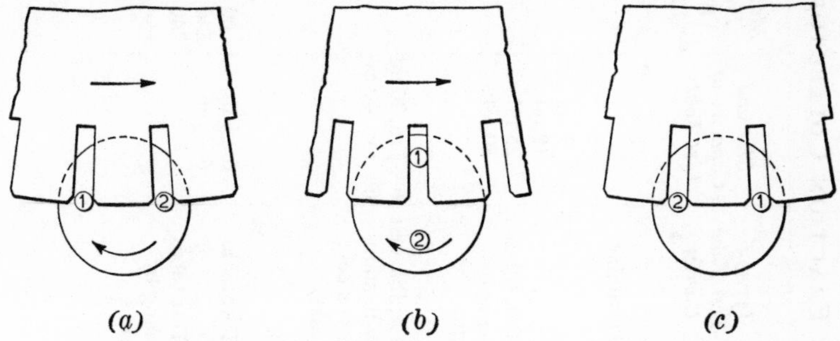

FIG. 3.15. Turntable drive with pegs and wide slots.
(*a*) Initial position when electric motor is first energized.
(*b*) Intermediate position, turntable moving at maximum speed.
(*c*) Final position, changeover complete, current switched off.

the pegs do not significantly affect correct positioning of the turntable.

An electric relay is often necessary in fraction collectors, enabling the very small current in the sensitive device which detects the completion of collection of a fraction (e.g. conductivity through the solution, photoelectric cell or drop counter) to switch the larger current needed for an electric drive. The Tektor capacity switch (Fielden, Ltd.) can be adjusted so that very small differences in the electrical capacity of a condenser, formed by metal plates attached to the terminals of the instrument, operate a mains voltage changeover switch. The instrument can be arranged to detect either passage of drops or the rise of liquid to a definite point in a tube. Alternatively, where the eluant is an electrolyte, a thyratron relay may be used.

The type of detector used to actuate the fraction collector should be considered in relation to the solvent and the substances being

Table 3.1. Commercial Fraction Collectors

Suppliers	Model	Method of Controlling Fraction Volume	Range	Type of Test Tube Carrier	Size and Capacity of Test Tubes	Max. no. of Fractions Without Attention	Additional Features
Aimer	Central	Photoelectric electronic drop counter or Volumetric siphon balance	1–999 drops 1, 2, 3, 5, 10 15, 25, or 50 ml siphon	Turntable Test tubes hang by rims	3 ml 10 ml 25 ml 50 ml	177 159 104 76	Siphon balance model switches to battery if mains fail Alternative photoelectric siphon available for use with volatile solvents
Baird and Tatlock	Mark 2	Volumetric vessel with inlet and outlet valves and photo-electric relay	1–60 ml continuously adjustable	Flexible belt with stainless steel links	$6\times\frac{5}{8}$ in. 20 ml 6×1 in. 60 ml	350 150	Belt loader available
L.K.B.	Radirac	Timer or Volumetric siphon balance or Photoelectric transistor drop counter	4–60 min 1·5, 2, 3, 5, 10, 15 or 25 ml 2^n drops (where n=2 to 7)	Turntable Test tubes hang by rims	$6\times\frac{1}{2}$ in. $6\times\frac{7}{8}$ in.	60 circular 240 spiral 240 square-wave	Detachable racks for 24 tubes available for use with square-wave operation Large volume attachment for max. of 30 1 litre fractions

Locarte	LTD/2	Timer	1–60 min	Turntable		80	Automatic turntable adjustment can be arranged to switch off at end of run
	LDC/1	Conductivity	1–100 drops	Tubes stand on solid base	$6 \times \frac{5}{8}$ in.	(160 with automatic turntable adjustment)	
	LDC/2	Photoelectric	1–100 drops				Electro-mechanical drop counter on LDC/1 and LDC/2
Shandon		Gravimetric test tube balance	1–15 ml	Turntable, tubes hang by rims	3 ml 15 ml	70 50	Switches off automatically at end of run
Towers		Volumetric siphon balance	1, 2·5, 5, 10, 25 or 50 ml	Turntable, tubes stand on solid base	$4 \times \frac{1}{2}$ in. $6 \times \frac{1}{2}$ in. 6×1 in.	100 spiral	

separated. Photoelectric drop counting is applicable both to the less volatile organic solvents and aqueous solutions. Drop counting or level-operated relays based on the conductivity of the eluant are restricted to electrolytes, and with these, care should be taken to ensure that a minute current (of the order of microamps) only, passes through the solution so that decomposition by electrolysis is reduced to negligible proportions. Platinum wire or foil is suitably inert for electrodes. Where contact with metal must be avoided altogether, a capacity switch with the electrodes placed outside the measuring vessel is suitable.

Home-made and Commercially Available Fraction Collectors. When first developed, fraction collectors were inevitably constructed in the laboratory, but during the last decade several types have become available commercially. The main design features of such collectors, readily available in this country, are summarized in Table 3.1.

When much chromatography is to be carried out, it is probably best to purchase a commercial instrument. Expense may be minimized, if workshop facilities and sufficient time are available, by constructing a collector to suit individual requirements. Experience has shown there may be some difficulty in completely eliminating potential mechanical breakdown. Sticking of the turntable during changeover is to be avoided at all costs. To ensure that this does not happen the basic design should be similar to one of the types already well-established. All working parts should be examined for reliability and bearing surfaces carefully smoothed and polished with fine emery paper. In marking out holes in the turntable it is important to check for cumulative errors by an independent method, before drilling. The finished instrument should be tested for several days with a dummy column and any residual faults rectified.

APPARATUS FOR PAPER CHROMATOGRAPHY

Tanks and Troughs

The tanks used for paper chromatography serve both to enclose the paper and, in descending chromatography, to support the trough which contains the solvent. Such tanks must be almost completely airtight so that the paper may be surrounded by air saturated with the vapour of the particular solvent being used. To avoid the necessity of waiting for the re-establishment of saturation of the air after the tank has been opened, the tank lid is often provided with a small hole through which solvent may be run into the trough. If possible the tank should be transparent to permit observation of the position of the solvent front.

Chromatography tanks are easily improvised in the laboratory. Consden, Gordon and Martin (1944) first used stoneware drain-pipes, but probably the most useful type consists of discarded battery jars (Fig. 3.16). Lids can be made from plate glass, ground on to the

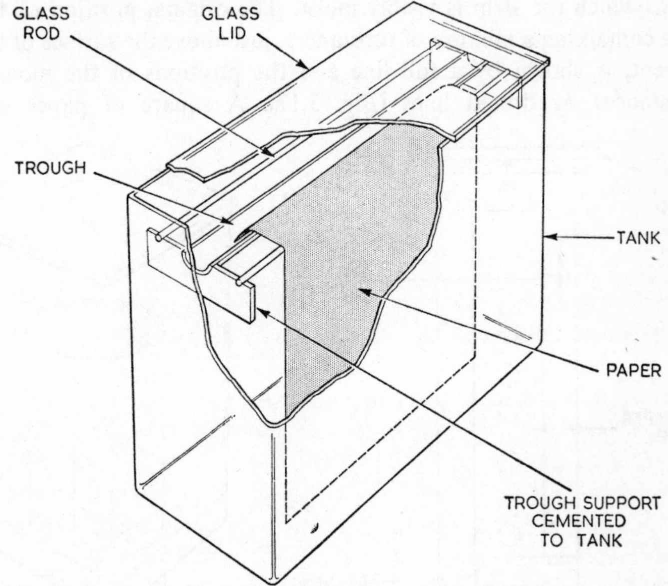

FIG. 3.16. Tank for descending paper chromatography, made from a battery jar.

tops of the jars with carborundum powder until a close fit is obtained. For descending chromatography, some means must be provided for supporting the solvent trough near to the top of the tank. In glass tanks, which are not easily drilled, wire frame supports standing on the bottom and rising almost to the full height of the tank are sometimes used, but these are somewhat cumbersome. Fortunately the use of Araldite epoxy-resin adhesive permits the cementing of suitably shaped supports to the glass.

Glass jars sufficiently large for papers more than 20 in. square may however be difficult to obtain. Large tanks may be constructed having sides of plate glass, but with ends, base and lid made of wood.

Well-waxed teak is probably most suitable, but unfortunately, when wood is used, some warping, with resultant leakage of vapour, may eventually take place.

Paper chromatography can be carried out with very simple equipment by using the ascending method. A strip is suspended by a hook from the ground-glass lid of a gas jar. The lower end of the paper dips into the solvent (moving phase) in the bottom of the jar. The solvent creeps up the paper by capillarity, keeping a straight front up to which the strip is visibly moist. The original position of the spot containing a mixture of substances, just above the surface of the solvent, is shown by a full line and the positions of the moving substances by dotted lines (Fig. 3.17). A square of paper can

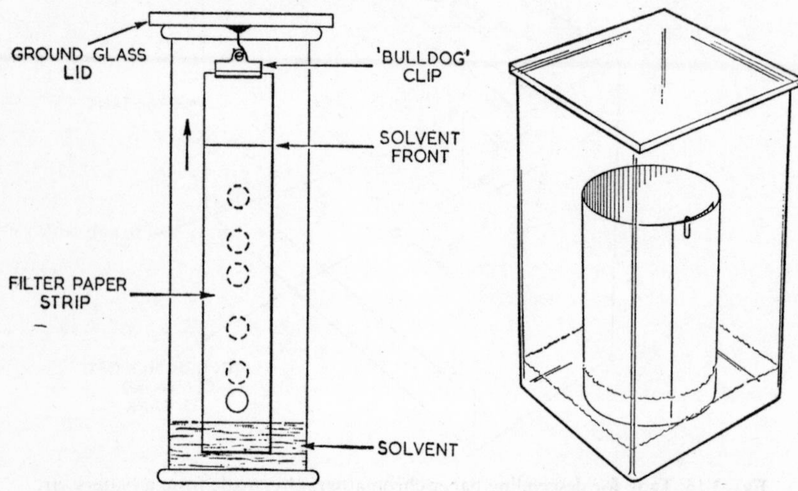

FIG. 3.17. Gas jar apparatus for ascending paper chromatography.

FIG. 3.18. Ascending paper chromatography with paper clipped into a roll.

be clipped into a cylinder, so that it will stand with its lower edge immersed in a layer of solvent in the bottom of a tank (Fig. 3.18). Datta, Dent and Harris (1950) introduced a special aluminium frame which enables a number of small (20 × 20 cm) two-dimensional chromatograms to be developed simultaneously by the ascending method in the same tank (Fig. 3.19).

In ascending chromatography, provision of a solvent trough presents no special problems. If the tank is made of glass, it may be filled with solvent to an appropriate depth or, alternatively, a suitable shallow glass dish (e.g. a Petri dish) may stand on the floor of the tank. For descending chromatography, on the other hand, a long, narrow trough is required (Figs. 3.16 and 3.20). Because of their

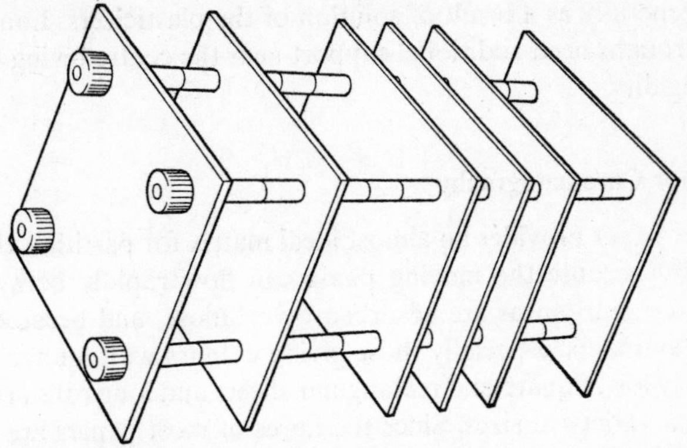

FIG. 3.19. Paper holder for developing a number of small, two-dimensional paper chromatograms simultaneously (Datta, Dent and Harris, 1950, *Science*, **112**, 621).

excellent chemical resistance, glass troughs have often been used, but unfortunately are very fragile in this shape. The supports at the top of the tank should therefore be very secure.

Originally glass troughs were made by grinding a slit in a piece of tubing which had been sealed at both ends, but this tedious process is no longer necessary, since glass troughs of a half-round section are now available commercially. Good quality stainless steel is suitable for use with non-corrosive solvents. This material is available in 'L' sections and can be made into troughs by welding-on triangular

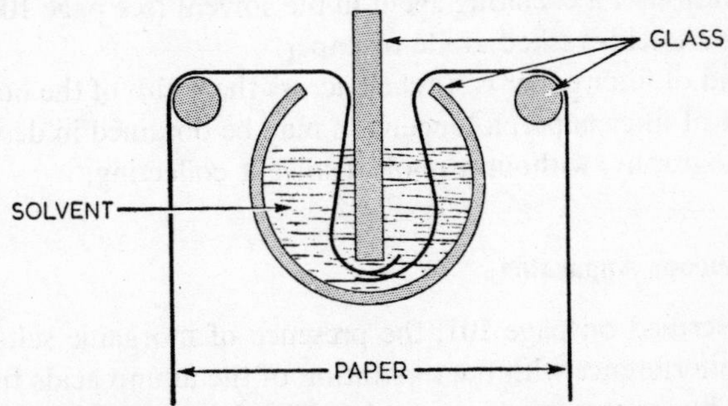

FIG. 3.20. Cross-section of glass trough, showing method of holding paper (Consden, Gordon and Martin, 1944, *Biochem. J.* **38**, 224).

end pieces. Unfortunately, phenol tends to attack the welded joints and so becomes coloured. Troughs can also be made from lengths of standard-section polythene. This material is inert to most solvents but may become slightly porous in the neighbourhood of welds, or more generally as a result of solution of the plasticizers. Long polythene troughs need additional support near the centre owing to their poor rigidity.

Paper for Chromatography

Filter paper provides an almost ideal matrix for partition chromatography because the moving phase can flow rapidly between the fibres, few substances are adsorbed by cellulose, and because levels of contaminants, especially those giving colours with ninhydrin, are relatively low. Square and rectangular sheets and long rolls are available in a variety of sizes. Since the fibres of most papers are preferentially oriented in one direction, the rate of solvent movement in a sheet is usually somewhat different in the two directions at right angles. The machine direction should be noted when deciding the direction of flow for the solvent.

Many types of paper are now available for chromatography. Much work, especially in Britain, has been carried out with Whatman papers, of which Grade No. 1 has certainly been widely used. For special applications, it may be necessary to select the most suitable grade. To assist in this choice, some of the characteristics of Whatman papers are listed in Table 3.2. The presence of small amounts of metal impurities in paper may sometimes be undesirable, but the effect of these can be reduced by washing the paper before use, by incorporation of a chelating agent in the solvent (see page 104) or by selecting an acid-washed grade of paper.

If a pad of filter paper is stitched across the width of the bottom of the sheet of filter paper, a longer run may be obtained in descending chromatography, without a pool of solvent collecting.

Miscellaneous Apparatus

As described on page 101, the presence of inorganic salts causes serious interference with the separation of the amino acids from one another by paper chromatography. The interfering salts may be removed before chromatography by means of an *electrolytic desalter*

Table 3.2. Characteristics of Whatman Papers and their Application in Chromatography

Grade No.	*Flow Rate*	*Paper Characteristics*	*Applications*
1	Medium	Smooth surface medium weight	Widely used for all types of chromatography
3HR	Fast	Heavier and denser than No. 1. Manufactured specially for paper chromatography. Gives good spot resolution	All types of chromatography
3MM	Faster than 3HR	Softer and smoother than No. 3HR; thick	Inorganic substances and electrophoresis. Will handle larger amounts than No. 1 or 4
4	Fast	Open texture medium weight	Widely used for amino acids, sugars, etc.
7	Medium fast	Rough surface	Intermediate in rate of solvent flow to Nos. 1 and 4
17	Medium	Soft paper very thick	For small scale preparative chromatography and electrophoresis
20	Very slow	Very uniform close texture	Produces very even and compact spots
31 extra thick	Rapid	Very thick, acid washed	Very widely used for electrophoresis
54	Rapid	Single acid washed, hardened, great wet strength	Widely used for sugar separations and impregnation with adsorbents such as alumina, starch, magnesia, etc.
540	Medium	Double acid washed and hardened (540, 541, 542)	These three grades are also used when minimum metallic impurity in the paper is required (540, 541, 542)
541	Rapid		
542	Slow		

without serious loss of amino acids (Consden, Gordon and Martin, 1947). In this apparatus, the solution to be desalted floats on a mercury cathode, and is separated from the carbon or platinum anode, by a Cellophane (or Viscap) membrane. When a current is passed, the cations (e.g. sodium) move to the cathode where they are discharged and dissolved in the mercury. Anions pass through the membrane to the anode where they are discharged, some of the products of reaction escaping as gas. The mercury is circulated by a lift pump operated by a stream of tap water. This serves to remove the dissolved metals, which react with the water, and also helps to cool the circulating mercury, and hence the solution. When desalting is complete, the current falls to a small fraction of its initial value.

Electrolytic desalters of this type are available commercially (The Locarte Co. Ltd. and Shandon) and may be used with 1–10 ml of solution. It is possible to remove the salt from 2 ml of 1 per cent sodium chloride solution in 20 min with a current of 0·5 A. In a recently-developed, simplified form of desalting apparatus (Baird and Tatlock, Ltd.), the solution is contained in a central compartment, separated from the anode and cathode compartments (which are furnished with platinum electrodes surrounded by dilute acid), by cation and anion exchange membranes respectively. This modification is well suited to the rapid desalting of small volumes of solution, and is claimed to give better recovery of arginine than the mercury type.

Capillary pipettes with very fine jets are useful for applying small volumes of the solutions needed for analysis to paper chromatograms. Such tubes can easily be made in large numbers by pulling out melting-point tubes in the flame of a microburner. They are then broken apart at the narrowest point, where a tiny scratch is made with a diamond. Alternatively, more permanent pipettes may be drawn down from thick-walled tubing, and the tips ground. Small pipettes calibrated in μl are obtainable for use where the volume applied to the paper must be known.

When the solution for chromatography is very dilute, it is sometimes necessary to repeat the application of a spot at the same point on the paper. As the solvent must be allowed to evaporate from each spot before applying the next portion of the solution, the process may become very tedious, especially with relatively non-volatile solvents such as water. Evaporation is considerably hastened in a current of air, which may be provided by means of a domestic *hair dryer*. If the substances under investigation are stable, warm air may be used. Alternatively, if the substances to be separated are dissolved in a highly volatile organic solvent, the solution may be applied by means of a wick.

After development of the chromatogram, the solvent must be removed before spraying with reagent to reveal the spots. Although very volatile solvents may be evaporated in a current of air at room temperature, it is usually necessary to hasten the process by heating. Thus, some form of *drying oven*, in which the chromatograms can be hung, is needed. Such ovens may be constructed from angle iron and asbestos board. The temperature should be adjustable up to a maximum of 110° C, but accurate control is not necessary. Since many of the solvents are unpleasant, it is advisable to fit an extraction fan.

The paper chromatogram is usually sprayed all over with a suitable reagent from an atomizer. The all-glass type of *sprayer* is best, since it does not corrode and is easily cleaned when changing from one solution to another. Small differences in the dimensions of the jet have a considerable effect on the fineness of the spray. If a compressor is not available, air pressure may be applied by means of a rubber bulb or the discharge side of a rotary-vacuum pump. Spraying should be done in a fume chamber to minimize inhalation of the droplets. Heating to reveal the spots may be carried out in the drying oven.

An *ultra-violet lamp* may be required for the examination of substances which fluoresce. Low-power lamps are made for this purpose (The Locarte Co. Ltd.) which have the advantages of cheapness and of being less likely to cause damage to the eyes in cases of accidental exposure (see also page 98).

A *microdensitometer* of the type used for sensitometric work with photographic emulsions can be used to measure the optical density at any chosen position on the chromatograms. Several instruments have been designed especially for use with paper strips from chromatograms, so that a continuous record of the colour density is obtained, along the length of the strip. The paper is first treated with a suitable organic liquid, such as paraffin oil, to make it translucent. It is then attached to a revolving drum or sliding carriage on the instrument. The paper strip is moved at constant speed so that it traverses a beam of light passing first through a narrow slit and then through the paper, before reaching a photocell or photomultiplier which responds to the final light intensity. In simpler instruments (Baird and Tatlock, Ltd.), galvanometer readings are taken intermittently at suitable points after temporarily stopping the traversing mechanism. More elaborate types of apparatus (Locarte-Laurence Recording Densitometer) continuously record the optical density in graphical form on a roll of paper moving at the same speed as the chromatogram. The measurements of spot size and density obtained with this type of apparatus form a basis for rapid quantitative methods in paper chromatography (see page 99).

A more precise type of densitometer has been designed by Lugg and McEvoy-Bowe (1961); this is for making single measurements at the position of maximum density, in the centre of coloured spots, on paper chromatograms. These workers have studied systematically the problems associated with the photometry of coloured materials on filter paper. They found that measurements of maximum density, made with a small circular densitometer aperture, were of greatest value, although these were complicated by textural variations in the paper and by light reflected back by the paper towards the source.

Their instrument is fitted with a microscope mechanical stage to which an excised portion of the chromatogram is attached by means of a sheet holder. The stage is racked to and fro until the position of maximum density for each spot is located; when this is found the reading is taken. The sheet is then removed from the instrument, bleached free from colour and replaced in an identical position, so that the 'blank' reading, associated with the paper itself, may be taken at exactly the same point as the initial reading of the spot density. This overcomes the effect of local irregularities in paper texture. Loss of light by back-reflection is minimized by the use of several sheets of backing paper and an efficient collimator system fitted with a reflector. This instrument functions less empirically than the slit types of scanning photometers and its performance conforms much more closely with Lambert–Beer law relationships.

REFERENCES

Consden, R., Gordon, A. H. and Martin, A. J. P. (1944). *Biochem. J.* **38,** 224.

Consden, R., Gordon, A. H. and Martin, A. J. P. (1947). *Biochem. J.* **41,** 590.

Datta, S. P., Dent, C. E. and Harris, H. (1950). *Science*, **112,** 621.

Gault, H. and Ronez, C. (1950). *Bull. Soc. chim. France*, 597.

Georges, L. W., Bower, R. S. and Wolfram, M. L. (1946). *J. Amer. chem. Soc.* **68,** 2169.
Hagdahl, L. (1954). *Science Tools*, **1,** 21.
Hagdahl, L. and Danielson, C. E. (1954). *Nature, Lond.* **174,** 1062.
James, A. T., Martin, A. J. P. and Randall, S. S. (1951). *Biochem. J.* **49,** 293.
Lugg, J. W. H. and McEvoy-Bowe, E. (1961). *Analyt. Chem.* **33,** 535.
Moore, S., Spackman, D. H. and Stein, W. H. (1958). *Analyt. Chem.* **30,** 1185, 1190.
Mowery, D. F. (1951). *J. Amer. chem. Soc.* **73,** 5047.

CHAPTER 4
ADSORPTION

Introduction to Adsorption Chromatography

Although chromatography based on adsorption is less often employed than either partition or ion-exchange chromatography it remains an important method especially for separation of coloured substances. One of the reasons why adsorption chromatography is relatively seldom used is because its underlying mechanisms are less well understood than are those involved in partition and ion-exchange chromatography. Furthermore, unlike the ion-exchange resins, the substances most commonly employed for the stationary phase are chosen on an empirical basis from the many available adsorbents, instead of being produced synthetically to meet predetermined requirements. Thus the adsorptive properties of the substances in general use are often not quite those which, if available in a suitable combination in one adsorbent, would give optimum separation of the components of the mixture under investigation. On the other hand adsorption chromatography has the advantage of very wide applicability since almost all classes of compound, with the exception of inorganic ions, show some degree of adsorbability. In general the usefulness of the method increases with the molecular size of the substances to be separated. Another advantage is that separation of stereoisomers by means of optically active adsorbents can often be achieved.

In the following pages some aspects of the behaviour of those adsorbents most commonly employed for chromatography will be described. An account will also be given of the conditions for optimum separation of the substances likely to be present during chromatography on columns of adsorbents.

As has been described on pages 15 and 20, a chromatogram can be developed in one of several different ways. Three of these have been widely used in adsorption chromatography, namely (1) frontal analysis, in which the solution to be analysed is fed continuously into the column and so-called 'retention volumes' are measured (cf.

page 23), (2) displacement development, in which a more strongly adsorbed displacing agent is fed into the column after the mixture undergoing separation, and (3) elution development, in which pure solvent is used to elute the various components of the mixture as separate bands. In this chapter most attention will be given to adsorption chromatograms of the third type. Displacement development will also be mentioned.

Mechanisms of Adsorption

Whether two or more components of a mixture can in practice be separated by adsorption chromatography depends on a number of factors, only certain of which are under the control of the experimenter. The most important of these is the strength with which each component of the mixture is adsorbed and its solubility in the solvents used for elution. The degree to which any particular substance is adsorbed depends on the type of bonds which can be formed between the solute molecules and the surface of the adsorbent. Different adsorbents are capable of forming different types of bond, so that before proceeding further, it is necessary to specify the adsorbent in question. Since almost all organic molecules, with the exception of saturated aliphatic compounds, are more or less strongly adsorbed by *alumina*, the properties of this adsorbent will be chosen for discussion.

Examination of the strengths of adsorption of the various classes of compound by alumina shows a clear correlation between ability to form hydrogen bonds and adsorbability. Evidently hydrogen bonds are by far the most important type of bonds concerned. Many molecules, especially those which are highly polar and those which contain aromatic nuclei, are strongly adsorbed by alumina because of their ability to act as hydrogen donors in the formation of hydrogen bonds. The acceptor is thought to be an oxygen atom of the alumina. Other molecules such as nitrobenzene act as hydrogen acceptors from the hydroxyl groups of the alumina. Non-polar, non-ionic molecules such as the aromatic hydrocarbons can also form bonds which involve electron donation by the solute, the more conjugated double bonds that are present, the stronger is the adsorption. The adsorptive sites for these bonds have been identified as the surface aluminium atoms of the alumina. When the solute is ionized the ability of alumina to act partly as an ion exchanger also becomes of importance. The general properties of ion-exchange systems are discussed in Chapter 6; here it is sufficient to mention that alumina can act as a cation exchanger and, after washing with an acid, as an anion exchanger. Only the protons or anions on the surface of the solid particles are exchangeable so that capacity is quite limited.

The strength of any given bond depends primarily on the nature of the substance being adsorbed. Bond strength is measured as the apparent affinity in kcal/mol. Values for some common substances are given in Table 4.1. The strength of binding by which any molecule

TABLE 4.1. COVERAGE OF ALUMINA POWDER (GRADE II) SURFACE BY ADSORBED MOLECULES*

Solute	*Solvent*	*Temperature °C*	*Coverage Factor†* *(Phenol =100%)*	*Apparent Affinity kcal/mol*
Phenol	Water	58	100	2·4
Cellobiose	Water	53	63·8	4·5
Resorcinol	Water	58	57·6	3·2
4-Nitroaniline	Ethanol/water (1:1)	20	34·4	3·9
cis-Azobenzene	Ethanol/water (4:1)	30	>27·3	3·2
4-Aminoazobenzene	Dioxane	58	4	4·8
Naphthalene	2,2,4-trimethyl pentane	20	>0·28	<3·8
Nitrobenzene	Ethanol/water (1:1)	20	0·04	4·0

* Adapted from E. Heftmann, 1961, *Chromatography*, p. 43 (Reinhold Publ. Corp., New York).
† Percentage of total surface covered.

is held on to an adsorbent must be distinguished from the factors which determine the amount of a substance which is bound. The number of available adsorption sites in fact decides the proportion of the surface of the adsorbent which can be covered with adsorbed molecules. The specific coverage is measured in cm^2/g of adsorbent but is better expressed as per cent of the surface area capable of being covered by phenol. This substance is assumed to give 100 per cent coverage. As may be seen in Table 4.1 the per cent for some compounds (e.g. naphthalene and nitrobenzene) is only about 1/1000 part of that found for phenol, in other words there are relatively very few sites on alumina which will accept such molecules. At the same time the affinity constant for nitrobenzene is actually higher than is that for phenol.

The uptake, therefore, of any substance by an adsorbent is determined by several factors which often vary independently of one another. As will be described below, the number of available adsorption sites can be varied at will by the manner of adsorbent pretreatment. In practice the degree of adsorption is estimated by shaking a known amount of the adsorbent with the solution containing the substance in question. Fifteen minutes is usually sufficient for the attainment of equilibrium; the fact that this is reached so rapidly suggests that adsorption takes place only on the surface and that there is little or no penetration into the pores. After this period the adsorbent is removed and the decrease in concentration of the solute is estimated. Data obtained at varying concentration of solute can be plotted as adsorption isotherms. Examples of certain isotherms have already been given (cf. page 28). In practical chromatography, considerable importance rests on the information which can be expressed as the isotherm of each component of a mixture. This is because the isotherms determine both the position and shape of the corresponding chromatographic bands. In adsorption chromatography, linear isotherms which correspond to symmetrically shaped bands are very rare. The isotherms of most compounds are only linear, or nearly so, at very low concentration. At higher concentrations the isotherm, viewed from above the line, is usually convex. This shape corresponds to bands with sharp fronts and elongated tails.

At this stage, some of the factors which may limit the success of chromatographic separation must be mentioned. For large molecules inconveniently long periods for the attainment of equilibrium may be required. Another difficulty is the fact that chemical changes may take place while a substance is in the adsorbed state. When a substance is undergoing purification by passage through a chromatogram, such a chemical change may be due to removal of inhibiting substances or may be initiated by the adsorbent. Furthermore, efficiency of separation may be affected by the formation of covalent bonds with the adsorbent. Any or all of these factors may cause the desorption isotherms to be somewhat differently shaped in comparison with the corresponding adsorption isotherms. Unfortunately very little work on desorption isotherms has been reported, however it has been shown that *p*-nitrophenol after having been adsorbed from water cannot be completely eluted by this solvent.

Activation of Adsorbents

Alumina, magnesia and similar inorganic adsorbents, and also charcoal, can be activated by heating and then cooling in a dry atmosphere. For alumina a temperature just below, but not exceeding, 700° C is suitable. Alumina trihydrate is thus dehydrated to yield γ-alumina plus aluminium monohydrate ($Al_2O_3.H_2O$), and in commercially available alumina, sodium carbonate (Na_2CO_3) also is always present. To prepare alumina of graded degrees of adsorptive strength the commercial material is raised to a red heat and then allowed to cool in a desiccator. This yields the most strongly adsorptive material. Less-adsorptive grades can then be obtained easily by leaving this alumina in a damp atmosphere until sufficient water has been taken up. The alumina should be stirred occasionally. The deactivation thus brought about is due to water molecules becoming attached at the most active adsorptive sites, which are believed to be the oxygen atoms. Alumina, after roasting to nearly 700° C, is more strongly adsorptive with respect to water molecules, yet such treatment renders it less adsorptive with respect to hydrocarbons. Although more sites are available for water on the freshly roasted adsorbent, hydrocarbons are less strongly adsorbed. Such behaviour indicates that water and hydrocarbon molecules must be taken up by different sites. Recent evidence suggests that hydrocarbons are adsorbed by aluminium atoms which bear a partial positive charge due to deformation of the crystal structure such as can occur during grinding of the adsorbent.

As mentioned above, one of the fundamental limitations of adsorption chromatography is its empirical nature. Adsorbents with suitable adsorptive properties have to be found and cannot, in general, be made with the properties necessary to achieve the separation of any given mixture of compounds. A few attempts have, however, been made to produce adsorbents capable of adsorbing specifically one or more of the substances which it is desired to separate. In particular this has been done with silica gel which for this purpose was prepared in the presence of ethyl orange or *p*-dimethylamino *p*-sulphonamido azobenzene. After these substances had been removed completely from the silica gels which had been made in their presence, each type of gel so produced retained a degree of preferential adsorption for the substances in whose presence it had been made, compared with its ability to adsorb methyl orange. On the other hand, gels made in the presence of methyl orange did not show any preferential adsorption. Silica gel prepared in the presence of *d*-camphorsulphonic acid showed some specific adsorption for this stereoisomer compared with the *l*-form.

Grading of Chromatographic Alumina, Magnesia, etc. in Respect of Adsorptive Power

This may be done by noting the behaviour of pairs of azo dyes dissolved in benzene on columns of the adsorbent (e.g. alumina) which is to be tested. Conditions must be standardized. A simpler test is to allow a 0·1 per cent solution of Sudan red, dissolved in petroleum ether, to run down a column packed with each adsorbent. The narrowness of the band is then a good indication of the strength with which the dye is being adsorbed.

Selection of Adsorbents of Correct Particle Sizes

Since adsorption is a surface phenomenon it is of importance that the powders used for chromatography should be ground sufficiently finely to have large surface areas. Alumina with surface area of between 6 and 9 m^2/g. will be found to be satisfactory. Such material can readily be obtained first of all by passage through a 150 mesh sieve; the part of such powder which is then retained by a 200 mesh sieve is taken for use in the columns. Alumina Merk, which has been standardized according to Brockmann, has a particle diameter which averages 7 μ. The sieving of powders can be avoided if, instead, fractionation by decantation is carried out. Since this process depends both on the size range and the specific gravity of the particles, it is somewhat empirical. It can be done either by repeated stirring and then pouring off the suspension of unwanted fine particles after successive intervals, or by continuous passage of water through an apparatus of the type shown in Fig. 6.2.

Eluting Agents

Several authors have prepared lists of eluting agents arranged in order of their eluting power. Unfortunately the order of eluting power of solvents observed in relation to a particular adsorbent is not necessarily the same when another adsorbent is substituted. This is comprehensible since the activity of an eluting agent is due to its own molecules becoming adsorbed. Competition at the active sites thus takes place between molecules of the solute and of the eluting solvent. Which of these is most strongly bound depends on the affinity constants for the two types of molecule. Since these may vary independently for each solvent–adsorbent pair, it is clear that the absolute eluting power is a property which can be related only to a single solvent–adsorbent pair.

Fortunately, however, the properties of the adsorptive sites of chemically similar adsorbents are sufficiently like one another for certain general rules to be of some value. The most important of these is the relationship between the eluting power and the dielectric constant of many solvents. Table 4.2 gives certain solvents arranged

TABLE 4.2. SOLVENTS ARRANGED IN ORDER OF INCREASING DIELECTRIC CONSTANT

Solvent	*Dielectric Constant*
Hexane	1·88
Carbon tetrachloride	2·24
Benzene	2·29
Ether	4·47
Chloroform	5·2
Ethyl acetate	6·11
Dichloroethane	10·4
Butanol 2	15·5
Acetone	21·5
Ethanol	26
Methanol	31·2

in order of increasing dielectric constant; Jaques and Mathieu (1946) have stated that for mixtures of steroids adsorbed on alumina, this order is the same as that of the increasing eluting power of these solvents. It should be noted, however, that when lipids are fractionated (Trappe, 1940) on aluminium silicate, ether is a more powerful eluant than choloroform whereas the reverse is true on alumina. If hydrogen bonds between solvent and adsorbent are easily formed, as takes place between acetone and the hydroxyl groups of silica, exceptions to the dielectric-constant rule are likely to occur.

The decision as to which solvent or solvents to employ for any given chromatogram is always difficult. Obviously a compromise must be sought so that the substances to be separated are all soluble and are slowly eluted without, at the same time, being made to travel too rapidly down the chromatogram. As will be described below, the best answer is often found to be the use of a series of solvents of increasing eluting power or of a mixture of gradually changing composition and increasing eluting power.

Use of More Than One Solvent for Elution

Solvents of increasing eluting power can, if desired, be used successively to give the so called stepwise elution. This procedure can only be recommended when there are very large differences between the adsorptive strengths by which the various components of the mixture undergoing separation are held on the chromatogram. It is suitable for use with coloured substances such as the mixtures of chlorophyll, xanthophyll, etc. found in green leaves. When there are only small differences between the adsorbability of the components, and especially where a considerable degree of tailing is occurring, the use of stepwise elution must be avoided because it will result in the formation of more than one band containing the same substance. The manner in which multiple bands can be formed by the addition of a new solvent, or as a result of the addition of increased concentrations of a more powerful eluting agent in a solvent mixture, is shown in Fig. 4.1. Such behaviour is characteristic of chromatograms in which the isotherms of the substances undergoing separation are convex.

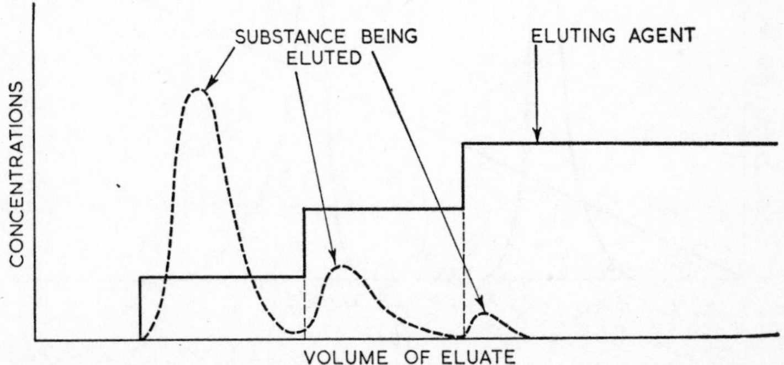

FIG. 4.1. Formation of more than one band of the same substance by the use of suddenly increased concentrations of eluting agent, so called *stepwise elution.*

Much better results can be expected if the increase in concentration of the eluting agent is brought about gradually. In the so-called gradient-elution method, a gradient of a new solvent is gradually introduced or the concentration of one already present at low concentration is gradually increased. In this way the eluting power of the mixture is steadily raised. By this means, given a suitable adsorbent, substances of very similar adsorbability can be separated. Because the eluting power of the mixed solvent is constantly increasing, the shapes of the bands on the column are very different from what they would be if elution were conducted with a solvent of constant eluting power. In Fig. 4.2 the changed shapes for bands corresponding both

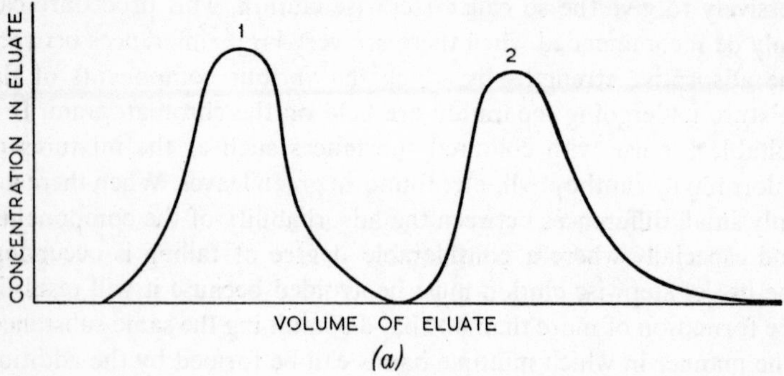

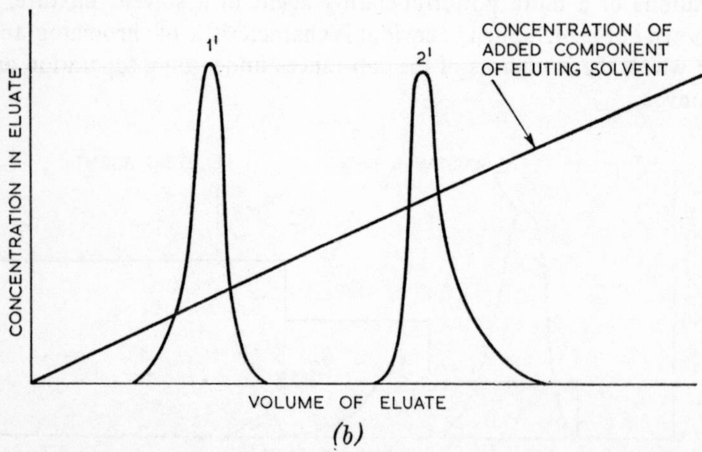

FIG. 4.2. Shapes of bands formed by eluting (*a*), with a solution of constant composition and (*b*), with a solution containing a gradually increasing concentration of the eluting agent.

to linear and convex isotherms are shown. If very steep gradients are used, double bands both containing the same solute can still be formed but in general the likelihood of such behaviour is very much reduced. Gradients can be produced most easily by means of a mixing vessel fitted with a stirrer as shown in Fig. 3.8. The steepness of such gradients is determined by relative sizes of the vessels and the ratio of the concentrations of the solutions initially present. A mixer of this type will give a gradient of the straight-line type, i.e. the concentration of the added eluant at any time will be proportional to the volume of liquid which has passed. Mixers have also been designed which will give any desired curved gradient. In certain cases, as in the chromatography of proteins, such non-linear gradients may be of great value.

Purity of Solvents

Because traces of impurities present in the solvents used either alone, or as components of mixtures, can make very considerable differences to the rates of elution, the purification of all solvents used for chromatography is of great importance. In addition, undesired chemical reactions on the chromatogram may well be promoted by impurities present in the solvents. Removal of such impurities is usually achieved by redistillation. Traces of peroxides may be removed by a preliminary passage of the solvent down a column packed with alumina.

Size and Shape of Columns

Long narrow columns packed with finely powdered adsorbents can be expected to give optimum separations. Unfortunately the flow rate through such columns may well be unduly slow. Even after application of pressure to speed up the flow rate, unacceptably long periods of time may elapse before the slower-moving bands can be expected to emerge. Thus in practice the length of the column will usually have to be reduced and the diameter increased to give sufficiently rapid flow rates. Shorter columns are also much more convenient to handle than are those of exceptional length. To achieve an increased flow rate it is better to shorten and broaden the column than to use a coarser grade of adsorbent because this would entail a reduced maximum permissible load for the column. The dimensions and flow rate finally chosen for any column must always represent a compromise between the various factors involved. If the chromatogram is used for the separation of coloured substances, so that after development the bands can be separated by cutting up the column, a long narrow shape is specially desirable. When columns of considerable diameter are employed it should be noted that, even though complete separation of bands on the column may have occurred, on elution some remixing is bound to take place. This is because in practice, bands of more or less irregular shape with non-level fronts always occur. That this effect is much less important when the same weight of adsorbent is packed into a longer and narrower tube is shown in Fig. 4.3.

Use of Coupled Columns

As has already been mentioned, the use of very long narrow columns is sometimes difficult or impossible. Fortunately some of the advantages of a long narrow column can be retained if the chromatogram is sub-divided into several sections of nearly similar length but of decreasing diameter (Fig. 4.4). Such chromatograms are effective because for good separation the bands need only be contained in a narrow column for the period just preceding their final emergence (cf. page 44). A chromatogram consisting of coupled columns is usually filled throughout with the same finely divided adsorbent. It should be noticed, however, that this design also makes possible the use, in series, of several different adsorbents in the one chromatographic system.

Size and Maximum Loading of Chromatograms

How large a chromatogram must be to separate given amounts of a pair of substances depends mainly on the adsorptive capacity of the material of which the column consists. This, of course, differs widely for each adsorbent, and for the substances being adsorbed. For alumina the specific surface covered by phenol is more than 2000 times greater than that covered by nitrobenzene (Table 4.1). These figures are an indication of the numbers of available adsorptive sites for each substance. Evidently when there are few adsorptive sites for any component great care must be taken not to overload the column in respect of the component in question. Unduly wide bands strongly

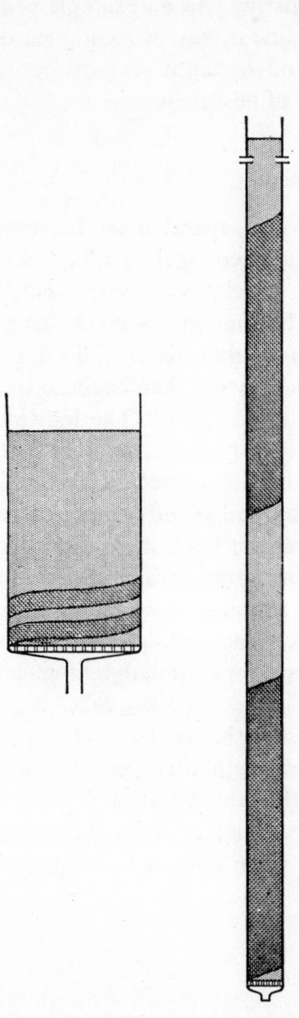

FIG. 4.3. Diagram to show that although bands may have become completely separated while contained in a chromatogram, yet after elution they will have become partially remixed. In the narrower column they remain separated even after elution. (Heftmann, 1961, *Chromatography*, p. 77, Reinhold Publ. Corp., N.Y.).

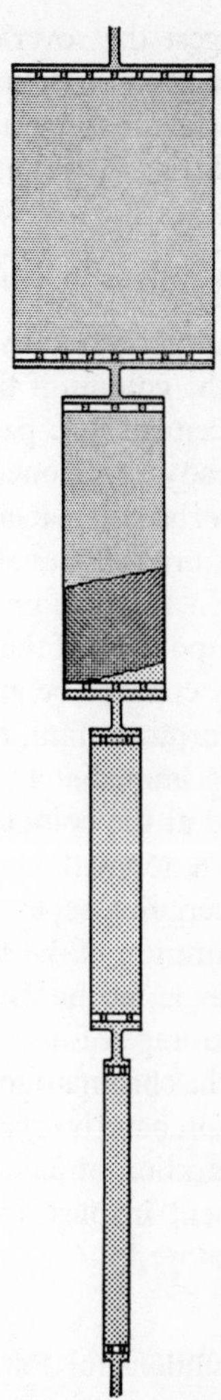

FIG. 4.4. Chromatogram divided into sections of successively decreasing diameter. In this design the sharpness of the band fronts is improved. (Heftmann, 1961, *Chromatography*, p. 81, Reinhold Publ. Corp., N.Y.).

suggest that overloading may be occurring. As an example of the capacity of a column of magnesium oxide it may be mentioned that satisfactory separations of β-carotene and the xanthines were reported by Strain (1942) at a level of 10 mg/g of adsorbent.

Separations by Displacement Development

Larger amounts of the substances to be separated can be applied to the column if the experiment is conducted by the method of displacement (cf. page 30) rather than by elution development. As already mentioned this is achieved by running a more strongly adsorbed displacing agent into the column immediately following the mixture to be analysed. The various substances then begin to travel down the column as a series of continuous bands. The individual components of the mixture continuously displace one another so that they come to be arranged in the order of their respective, increasing, adsorption affinities with the most strongly adsorbed component running immediately in front of the displacer. Even if no displacer is used at the commencement of a chromatogram, which is developed by elution with pure solvent, some interaction between the substances undergoing separation is bound to take place. Only after complete separation of the bands do the conditions for elution development as a single mechanism of separation become established. Since a great advantage of displacement development is that rather heavy loading of the chromatogram is permissible, this method is specially suitable for preparative scale experiments. On the other hand, since complete separation of bands does not take place, the recoveries of each component in pure form are lower than when elution development is employed.

Conditions for Extrusion of Chromatograms

Once a correct ratio for the weight of the solutes and the adsorbent has been reached, the question as to how large a column should be used can be decided by the physical convenience of the apparatus. If only small amounts of material are available for analysis, the size should be correspondingly reduced, the limit being the sensitivity of the means for detection of the material of each separated band.

If the bands on a chromatogram are adequately separated but move slowly, it is often convenient to extrude the column of adsorbent from the tube before elution is attempted. When the column has been successfully extruded, the bands may be separated from one another very simply by mechanical division. Elution of each band can then easily be carried out. Alternatively it may sometimes be better to dissolve the adsorbent, e.g. sucrose, inorganic salts, etc., and leave the band material in insoluble form; whichever method is chosen it is of great importance to achieve a clean and neat extrusion of the adsorbent from the tube. This can be done more easily if the bottom layer of the adsorbent rests on a removable porous plate rather than on glass wool. Before extrusion is attempted, air should be allowed to enter the column, suction being applied if necessary. After the chromatogram has thus been freed as far as possible from the solvent, the bottom plate is pressed upwards with a rod. If difficulty is experienced in extruding a given chromatogram it may be necessary to use a glass tube of slightly conical shape. Alternatively, with very narrow columns and coloured substances the glass tube in which the chromatogram has been contained can be cut at appropriate levels, thus separating the various bands from one another.

Methods of Packing of Columns

Dry Packing. This method is sometimes used for columns made from magnesia or alumina. Its only advantage is to ensure that the adsorbent is tightly packed into the column. For this purpose a tamping rod is used and tamping is repeated a number of times after successive additions of small amounts of the adsorbent. The disadvantage of this method is that large volumes of solvent must be run through the column to ensure complete removal of all air bubbles. Some time can be saved by the removal of dissolved air from the solvent before it is used for this purpose.

Wet Packing. Successful results may often be achieved by the simple method of pouring a well-mixed slurry of the adsorbent into the tube and following it up at once with the solvent. Unless the adsorbent is specially finely divided it is necessary to take care that air should not be drawn into the packed chromatogram; this can readily be achieved by ensuring that the level of the solvent is always above that of the surface of the adsorbent. When a specially evenly packed column is desired the following method may be adopted. The tube is first almost completely filled with solvent which is allowed to run out rather slowly. Then without delay a little of the slurry is poured in so that the adsorbent settles through the solvent and begins to form a bed at the bottom of the tube. Such additions are repeated at frequent intervals. Evenness of packing can be improved still further if an extension tube is fitted to the top of the chromatogram so that the adsorbent falls through a greater height of solvent. In this way any unevenness in packing due to irregularities in the slurry can be obviated. Finally sufficient solvent must be run through the packed column to ensure that no further contraction of the solid phase takes place during use.

Checking on a Column Before Use

Successful chromatography depends very largely on the uniformity and regularity of distribution of the adsorbent in the column. Some idea as to whether, in fact, a chromatogram is packed sufficiently evenly can be obtained by a preliminary addition to the column of a solution containing a few milligrammes of a non-adsorbed or lightly-adsorbed coloured material. If a regularly shaped and only slightly tipped band is thus obtained, the column can be passed for use. Some notice of the volume of solvent required to elute the test band should also be taken because bands having a conical shape may often be encountered. In such cases, even though a regular ring of colour is seen as the band passes down the tube, the material adsorbed on the central core may be much retarded. One of the reasons for this type of behaviour is a slight contraction of the packed adsorbent, due to dehydration consequent upon the use of a solvent which is less saturated with water than is the adsorbent.

Application of the Mixture to be Analysed to the Chromatogram

Optimum separations will be obtained if the mixture of substances to be analysed is applied to the column in the smallest possible volume of solvent. If possible, the solvent should be the one with which elution is to be carried out. Care must be exercised to ensure that the whole of the sample to be analysed is in solution, since any solid accidentally transferred to the column will dissolve gradually and thus produce a band or bands with very long tails. In some cases it is permissible to transfer the material to be analysed to the column in a different solvent from the one which is to be used for development of the chromatogram. A solvent of this type, however, must not have a much greater eluting power than the first of the solvents to be used for elution. Before transfer of the sample, the solvent level should be allowed to run down until the surface of the adsorbent has just been reached. Transfer can be made most easily by means of a pipette with a tip bent at right angles; the solution is allowed to run from this on to the wall of the tube at a point just above the surface of the adsorbent. As soon as the solution containing the sample has soaked into the adsorbent it is followed by a small volume of wash liquid from the vessel which previously contained the sample. The washing process is repeated two or three times. After the last lot of washings has soaked into the adsorbent, the column is filled with pure solvent. With lightly packed adsorbents it is sometimes worth covering the surface with a circle of filter paper to prevent disturbance during transfer of the sample and washings to the column.

Methods for the Detection of Bands

When colourless substances are subjected to chromatography they must either be converted to a coloured derivative on the column or detected in the eluates by some suitable test. The coloured derivatives can be formed on the column after it has been extruded from its tube. For this purpose a suitable colour reagent is rapidly brushed along the full length of the chromatogram. Alternatively colourless substances can be made to reveal their positions because of their ability to quench the fluorescence of a dye which is irreversibly adsorbed on the column. For alumina, magnesium oxide and calcium carbonate columns, Brockmann and Volpers (1947) have found the dye, morin, to be suitable, berberine is effective with silica. Similar effects can also be obtained by mixing finely-powdered luminous paint with the adsorbent. When colourless materials are likely to be contained in the eluate from a chromatogram it is necessary to use a fraction collector (page 53). Investigation of the fractions may then be done in any one of numerous ways. The simplest method is by weighing after complete removal of solvent from each fraction. Alternatively, measurement of the adsorption of ultra-violet light will often be useful. Finally it may be necessary to take an aliquot from each fraction and convert the material to a coloured compound by the addition of a suitable reagent.

TABLE 4.3. LIST OF ADSORBENTS

Adsorbent	*Suitable for Separating*	*Strength of Adsorbent*
Alumina	General	Strong
Bauxite	Enzymic hydrolysates of chitin, sugar	Strong
Aluminium silicate	Sterols and sterol glycosides	Medium
Magnesia	Carotenoids and many other substances separable on alumina	Strong
Magnesium silicate	Sugar acetates Steroids Acetylated glycosides	Strong
Calcium hydroxide	Carotenoids	Strong
Calcium carbonate	Xanthophylls, naphthoquinones	Medium
Tricalcium phosphate	Proteins	Medium
Calcium oxalate	Anthraquinones	—
Silica gel	Sterols, fatty acids, glycerides Sugar acetates Terpenes	Strong
Fuller's earth (magnesium alumino-silicates)	Basic amino acids, pteridines	Strong
Anhydrous copper sulphate	Azobenzene derivatives	—
Charcoal	Sugars, amino acids, branched from straight chain hydrocarbons	Strong
Sucrose	Chlorophyll, xanthophylls	Weak
Cellulose	Sugars, dyes	Weak

REFERENCES

Brockmann, H. and Schodder, H. (1941). *Chem. Ber.* **74,** 73.

Brockmann, H. and Volpers, F. (1947). *Chem. Ber.* **80,** 77.

Cassidy, H. G. (1957). 'Fundamentals of Chromatography', Vol. X of *Techniques of Organic Chemistry*, ed. by A. Weissberger, Interscience, New York.

Heftmann, E. (Ed.) (1961). *Chromatography*, Reinhold Publ. Corp., New York.

Jaques, J. and Mathieu, J. P. (1946). *Bull. Soc. chim., France*, 94.

Strain, H. H. (1942). *Chromatographic Adsorption Analysis*, Interscience, New York.

Trappe, W. (1940). *Biochem. Z.* **305,** 150.

CHAPTER 5

PAPER CHROMATOGRAPHY

Introduction to Paper Chromatography

Among the special advantages of chromatography on filter paper are its rapidity and convenience. The working time needed to carry out a single-dimensional analysis in a laboratory already suitably equipped is not much more than five minutes. No special skill is required and only rather simple apparatus (Figs. 3.16 to 3.20). As already mentioned, as little as a few microgrammes of the mixture to be analysed is sufficient. Only when a quantitative analysis is made must considerable care be taken at each step.

METHODS

Single-dimensional Chromatograms

Analysis, by the single-dimensional technique, of either a single sample on a strip, or several on a broader sheet of filter paper, involves four essential steps (Consden, Gordon and Martin, 1944):

(1) A volume of the solution to be analysed, small enough to form a wet spot of not more than 1–1·5 cm diameter, is applied a few centimetres from one end of the strip of filter paper.

(2) The end of the strip which now carries the spot of the sample solution is then inserted into a suitable trough containing the developing organic solvent. The end of the paper is held in the trough so that the solvent can gradually percolate by capillarity down the length of the strip as it hangs from the trough. To prevent evaporation from the strip both trough and strip are kept in a closed chamber, the atmosphere inside having previously been allowed to become saturated with solvent and water vapour. Alternatively the need for a special trough for the solvent may be avoided by placing a layer of the liquid directly in the bottom of the chamber and standing in it a rolled-up sheet of filter paper so that its lower edge is wetted by the solvent. Since, in this arrangement, solvent ascends through the

filter paper it is referred to as the *ascending method* (Figs. 3.17 and 3.18).

(3) After sufficient travel of the solvent through the pores of the filter paper, but before the solvent front has quite reached the far end of the strip or sheet, the chromatogram is removed from the chamber and dried.

(4) Finally, the strip is treated with a reagent suitably chosen to give coloured spots with some or all of the substances undergoing separation. This may be done either by spraying with a solution of the colour reagent or by dipping the paper into a similar solution. Often a final drying and heating stage is needed to hasten the reaction between the colour reagent and the substances on the filter paper which are thus revealed as coloured spots.

Permissible Amounts of Substances for Analysis which may be Applied to Single-dimensional Chromatograms

The upper limits of the amounts which can usefully be applied to strips of filter paper are determined by many factors, some of the more important of which are as follows:

(1) The difference in the R_f values of the substances concerned.
(2) Time available for development.
(3) Presence or absence of interfering substances.
(4) The thickness of the filter paper.

Without knowledge of the particular mixture to be separated and some of the other variables, only very approximate suggestions for the amount to be applied to the origin of a single-dimensional chromatogram can be made (0·1–0·2 mg). Where greater amounts are to be separated, the solution should be applied as a line parallel and close to the top or, in the case of ascending chromatography, bottom of the paper. An advantage of the application of the sample as a line is that, after development and drying, the edges and a narrow strip from the centre of the chromatogram can be cut off and stained as guides for the location of those areas containing the separated substances.

Two-dimensional Chromatograms

The technique is similar to that described above for the single-dimensional chromatogram except that square or rectangular sheets of filter paper are employed. The drop of solution to be investigated is applied at a point a few centimetres from one corner of the sheet leaving sufficient space for first one and then the second edge of the paper to be placed in troughs of the developing organic solvent. After development with the first solvent, the substances being separated form a row of spots, either completely or incompletely separated, near one edge of the sheet of paper. At this stage the sheet of paper is thoroughly dried since traces of the first solvent generally have an adverse effect on the separations occurring with the second solvent. After drying, the sheet with the partially separated substances, present as an invisible row of spots, is hung from the trough so that the second solvent can percolate through the paper. When this solvent has advanced far enough the sheet is ready for final drying, application of colour reagent, or other treatment.

A general advantage of the two-dimensional method is that larger quantities of material, applied as a single spot, can be completely separated as compared with chromatograms which have been developed in one direction only. This is especially true in the presence of contaminants such as traces of salts. Because sufficient separation occurs in the first dimension, much more successful chromatography is achieved with the second solvent. The very wide adaptability of two-dimensional chromatography is mainly due to the many possible pairs of solvents which may be chosen to separate particular mixtures of substances. Appropriate choice of solvents will be indicated in the sections dealing with each class of compound.

Two-dimensional Separations: Electrophoresis and Chromatography

Because many of the substances which can be separated by paper chromatography are ionized when in solution, an electrophoretic separation is often a useful preliminary stage. Full description of two-dimensional separations of this kind would require details concerning electrophoresis which are outside the scope of the present book. It may be mentioned, however, that the electrophoretic separation which requires as little as two hours, can be carried out before or after chromatography. The chromatography can be terminated after a period of 16–18 h so that the whole process of separation can be carried through in part of a day and one night. For optimum results, electrophoresis should be carried out first so that the line of spots thus produced need not be disturbed, as may happen when buffer is applied to the paper between chromatography and electrophoresis. Since the presence of salt is disadvantageous for chromatography, buffers containing only volatile materials must be used for the electrophoresis if this stage is carried out first. The patterns thus obtainable from enzymatic hydrolysates of proteins, for example, have been called 'fingerprints'. Under optimum conditions of resolution as many as 80 well-separated spots can be obtained (Katz, Dreyer and Anfinsen, 1959).

Reversed-phase Chromatography

Paper chromatography is essentially a technical means by which partition chromatography can be carried out. The stationary phase is usually aqueous and is held in the cellulose fibres while the moving phase is an organic solvent. Since most of the water in the system normally occurs in the cellulose fibres, substances with partition coefficients favouring water exist mainly in the stationary phase and move relatively slowly down the chromatogram. Most substances for which paper chromatography is useful, in fact have partition coefficients of this kind and thus can be separated by systems with organic solvents as the moving phase. Examples of such solvent systems are given on page 104.

Paper chromatography of substances with partition coefficients which favour the organic solvent phase can, however, also be successfully carried out. For this purpose a so-called reversed-phase system must be used. In this type of paper chromatography, the fibres of the paper are made to hold the organic solvent phase by pretreatment with a hydrophobic substance such as rubber, Vaseline, the ester of a higher fatty acid, or a silicone. Several grades of silicone-treated paper (Whatman Nos. 1, 4, and 20) suitable for reversed-phase chromatography are available commercially. Alternatively some of the hydroxyl groups of the cellulose can be substituted with acetyl groups. This yields paper with properties intermediate between normal paper and silicone treated paper. It should be noted that such acetylated papers cannot be used with chloroform because of their undue solubility in this solvent.

Methods using papers pretreated in this way (Block *et al.*, 1958) have been available for some time for separation of esters of fatty acids, dinitrophenylhydrazones, etc., but have not been used on such a wide scale as has been true of many other paper chromatographic methods. More recently, however, reversed-phase paper chromatography has been extended to include the barbiturates and certain other types of heterocyclic compound. For this purpose, paper pretreated with 10 per cent tributyrin in acetone has been found to be very suitable. Development with 0·07M phosphate buffer at pH 7·4 and 80–90° C has permitted adequate separation of the various barbiturates in less than half an hour. The rapidity of separation of these toxicologically important compounds, which has been made possible by the rather high temperature employed, is a most valuable feature of this method.

Methods for the Detection of Spots

After separation by chromatography, the various substances undergoing analysis will have migrated to a number of more or less well-separated areas of the filter paper. With colourless substances the positions of these areas, or pattern of spots, can be revealed by one of two general methods; either light of an appropriate wavelength may show up the spots as fluorescent areas, or they may be revealed indirectly by photography. Alternatively, by treatment with an appropriate reagent, the material present in any given spot may be converted to another substance, which is itself visible or which can be detected indirectly. In Table 5.1 some of the many methods available for the detection of amino acids and certain substances of rather similar type are listed. The usefulness of any of these methods will often depend on their specificity for the substances undergoing separation. When it is known that only the members of a single class of substances are present the use of only one colour reagent should be sufficient. With more complex mixtures and especially if it is desirable to reveal spots corresponding to every substance which has been separated, it may be necessary to prepare several chromatograms, each of which can then be treated with a different colour reagent. Any assumption that every spot has necessarily been revealed must, however, be avoided. The presence on a chromatogram of unrevealed spots is to be suspected if certain of the coloured areas are distorted from the normal round or oval shape.

The choice of the detection method will depend on the following considerations.

First, on the nature of substances present on the paper. Second, such methods must be sufficiently sensitive to reveal the positions

TABLE 5.1. REAGENTS USEFUL FOR IDENTIFICATION OF INDIVIDUAL AMINO ACIDS

Amino Acid	*Reagent**	*Colour*	*Minimum quantity (μg) required to give a just visible spot*
Arginine	Sakaguchi. α-naphthol in N.NaOH followed by sodium hypochlorite	Red	10
Citrulline	Ehrlich. *p*-dimethylamino-benzaldehyde in N.HCl	Yellow	
Cystine Cysteine Methionine	Platinic iodide. Platinic chloride and potassium iodide in acid acetone	White on purple background	
Homocysteine	Ninhydrin followed by dilute mercuric nitrate	Red sur-rounded by blue	
Histidine	Pauly. Diazotized sulpha-nilamide followed by sodium carbonate	Cherry red	
Glycine Histidine Tryptophan	Zimmerman. *o*-phthaldialde-hyde in acetone. Heated to 50° C		
Ornithine	2% vanillin in n-propanol followed by 1% potassium hydroxide	Yellow brown	0·5
Sarcosine	2% vanillin in n-propanol followed by 1% potassium hydroxide	Red	
Phenylalanine	Ninhydrin followed by sodium bicarbonate	Blue	
Proline Hydroxyproline	0·2% isatin in acetone. Heat at 70–76° C	Blue†	1–5

TABLE 5.1 (*cont.*)

Hydroxyproline	Isatin followed by freshly prepared *p*-dimethylamino-benzaldehyde in acid acetone	Purple red	0·1
Serine Threonine	Nessler's reagent almost saturated with sodium periodate	Yellow	
Taurine	0·2% *o*-phthalaldehyde plus 0·2% urea in acetone. Heat at 50° C followed by 1% alcoholic potassium hydroxide. Reheat	Red	
Tryptophan and other indoles	Ehrlich. 1% *p*-dimethyl-aminobenzaldehyde in HCl acetone	Purple	
Tyrosine	0·1% α-nitroso-β-naphthol in 95% ethanol. Followed by 10% aqueous nitric acid. Heat		1–2

* Further details of these reagents are given in Block, Durrum and Zweig, 1958, 2nd ed., pages 128–39.
† Other amino acids give pink or blue colour.

of the substance at the concentration actually available. Thirdly, the detection method will depend on whether simple spot location is all that is required or whether quantitative estimation is to be attempted. Accurate quantitative measurements can most easily be made when some property such as the absorption of ultra-violet light or radioactivity can be utilized without removal of the separated substance from the paper. If the usual method of conversion of colourless to coloured substances, by spraying the paper with a suitable reagent, is to be used quantitatively the conditions of colour development must be strictly controlled. This applies to photometric estimation of the coloured substance both on the paper and after preliminary elution (cf. Quantitative Methods, page 108).

The Use of Ultra-violet Light. Spots formed by substances with strong absorption in the ultra-violet can usually be observed directly as dark areas when a chromatogram is illuminated with light of appropriate wavelength. For this purpose a lamp with strong emission at 254 mμ is suitable. Under ultra-violet illumination using a 365 mμ source the positions of many other substances are also revealed owing to their ability to fluoresce or to quench the background fluorescence of the filter paper. Such effects are greatly reduced by residues, which may remain in the paper after the use of certain organic solvents, or by traces of moisture, but when the chromatograms have been thoroughly dried, slight structural differences between the substances forming the spots as, for instance, those between the various derivatives of indole (Block *et al.*, page 316) may result in useful differences in colour. Permanent records of the location and intensity of all spots which either absorb or are fluorescent in ultra-violet can be obtained conveniently by means of contact photography. For those substances which fluoresce in light of wavelength below 405 mμ, a Kodak 2A gelatin filter should be interposed between the light source (365 mμ) and the photographic film (Abelson, 1960).

Detection of Radioactivity. Areas of radioactivity on chromatograms can be revealed either by autoradiography or by means of a Geiger-Muller tube or other instrument suitable for the detection of the expected radiation. The latter technique is somewhat more sensitive, especially with the more penetrating kinds of radiation. Quantitative results can be obtained readily from both single- and two-dimensional chromatograms by the use of the instruments now available. The production of autoradiographs requires little specialized apparatus and involves a minimum of working time; the optimum exposure time for the autoradiography of a given chromatogram should, however, always be carefully determined.

Detection of Substances Required for, or Inhibiting the Growth of Micro-Organisms. After thorough drying, any chromatogram expected to include spots of such substances is placed on the surface of a slab of agar jelly which has previously been seeded with the appropriate sensitive organism. The location of the areas occupied by growth stimulators or inhibitors is then gradually revealed as these substances diffuse from the spots into the agar. To shorten the diffusion path from each spot a single-dimensional chromatogram may be divided longitudinally from the point of origin. This has the advantage that the remaining half may then be used for colour development or other location technique.

Detection Methods Involving Chemical Modification of the Substances to be Located. Chemical modification of the separated substances which form the pattern of spots on a chromatogram is most conveniently achieved by lightly spraying the dry paper with a solution containing the appropriate colour reagent, Table 5.1. Conversion to coloured derivatives then occurs, either immediately as the solvent evaporates, or more slowly, or after heating. The same result may also be achieved by dipping the sheet in a bath of the reagent solution. This method ensures even application over the whole area of the sheet, but is less widely used than spraying because it leads to blurring and loss of colour unless the substances from which the spots are composed are completely or almost completely insoluble in the solvent in question. Information concerning the optimum conditions for carrying out these processes is given below in relation to chromatograms of the amino acids. The techniques for application of colour reagents suitable for location of other classes of compound are very similar.

Quantitative Methods. Numerous methods for the quantitative estimation of individual substances after separation by paper chromatography have been described. It should be recognized, however, that quantitative paper chromatography is specially suitable only when extremely limited amounts of the materials for analysis are available, or when the properties of the substances concerned are such that they can be readily estimated while still on the paper. Thus accurate analyses of nucleotides and other ultra-violet absorbing substances can be made quite easily after separation on paper chromatograms (cf. page 116). In practice, accuracy is most seriously limited by variation between one chromatogram and another. Many attempts at improvement by the use of replicate chromatograms have been made but, unfortunately, by this approach the working time is always increased. If approximate quantitative results are all that are required (within 10–20 per cent), they can be obtained without much difficulty in single-dimensional chromatograms by the use of varying amounts of suitable standards, applied to nearby areas of the same paper and therefore subject to similar conditions during chromatography and colour formation. Photometry of the coloured substances can be carried out either on the paper or after elution. Although photometric measurements of such eluates can be carried out with great accuracy, quantitative photometry of the spots while still on the chromatogram is preferable because of its simplicity. Where possible, the conversion of colourless to coloured substances before chromatography, rather than after, is advantageous for quantitative work. If this is done, the conditions for quantitative conversions can be much more readily controlled and, in addition, no further treatment is required for the location of the separated spots. On the other hand, the use of a large coloured substituent group is likely to decrease differences between R_f values. Quantitative estimation of the solutions obtained by the elution of individual spots may be easily carried out if recovery of the separated substances is already being undertaken for some other purpose. In such cases an aliquot of the eluate may be used for quantitative estimation, or, after measurement of a physical property, the whole of the eluted material may be available for further investigation. For details of the most appropriate method for quantitative analysis following chromatography on paper, see under the chromatography of each class of substances described in the text which follows.

AMINO ACIDS AND PEPTIDES

Introduction

Complete separation of almost all of the amino acids can be achieved with little difficulty by paper chromatography. For this purpose various readily available organic solvents, or mixtures of solvents can be used. The conditions under which the separations can be carried out can be varied within quite wide limits. On the other hand, for optimum spacing of the spots and ease of operation, the systems described below (page 104) have been found to be specially useful. Any two of the amino acids, even if they are of very similar structure, can be separated by chromatography with a single solvent. When, however, more complex mixtures such as those consisting of the 17–18 amino acids which are obtained on hydrolysis of proteins are to be examined, the two-dimensional method becomes necessary.

The separation of the mixtures of peptides formed when proteins are incompletely hydrolysed with acid or alkali, or are subjected to proteolysis by means of enzymes, represents an even more difficult problem due to the very large number of individual substances which are likely to be present. Furthermore the differences between the partition coefficients characteristic of individual peptides are generally much smaller than those between the amino acids; as a result, with the larger peptides separations become increasingly difficult.

Sample Preparation

If applied to the paper at such a concentration that the diameter of the initial wet area does not exceed approximately 1 cm, 20–50 μg of most of the amino acids will form strongly-coloured spots of convenient size (approximately 2 × 2 cm) after chromatography and treatment with ninhydrin. Thus each amino acid in the solution to be analysed should be present at a concentration of about 1 per cent. Lower concentrations are permissible down to the limit of sensitivity of the colour-reaction employed. For the amino acids detected with ninhydrin, the minimum quantities which will lead to the formation of just visible spots are given in Table 5.2. Repeated application and drying-off of more dilute solutions on the same area of the paper is sometimes undertaken. If more concentrated solutions of the amino acids are used so that quantities well above 50μg of each are applied, resolution will be impaired due to the increased size of the final spots; however, considerably heavier loading is possible when thick paper such as Whatman 3 MM is used.

Another condition for the formation of well-separated and undistorted spots is that the concentration of inorganic salt or other contaminant in the solution for analysis should not be much higher than that of the amino acids. Any considerable concentration of salt will reveal itself during the development of the chromatogram by the formation of easily seen, waterlogged areas. Where this has happened the organic-solvent phase is separated from the paper by a film of liquid water. If distortion from this cause is to be expected a trial chromatogram may be developed for a short distance. Suitable desalting procedures may then be applied to the main bulk of the solution if any waterlogged areas are seen to have appeared. Techniques for this purpose are given on page 68. Somewhat higher concentrations of salt are permissible when Whatman 3 MM paper is used instead of a thin paper.

Choice of Filter Paper (See Table 3.2)

Chromatographic separation of most of the amino acids can be achieved by the use of almost any type of filter paper. For optimum

TABLE 5.2. JUST DETECTABLE QUANTITIES OF SOME AMINO ACIDS AND PEPTIDES BY NINHYDRIN ON TWO-DIMENSIONAL CHROMATOGRAMS USING PHENOL, COLLIDINE-LUTIDINE

Compound	*Minimum Quantity* (μg)	*Colour of Spot*
Alanine	0·2	Purple
Alanylglycine	3	Pink purple
α-Amino-n-butyric acid	0·2	Purple
Arginine.HCl	4	Blue purple
Asparagine	1	Brown yellow
Aspartic acid	0·4	Blue
Cysteic acid	8	Blue
Glucosamine.HCl	4	Purple brown
Glutamic acid	0·1	Purple
Glutamine	2	Purple
Glutathione	10	Blue purple
Glycine	0·1	Pink purple
Histidine.HCl	25	Brown
Hydroxyproline	1	Brown yellow
Isoleucine	0·5	Purple
Leucine	0·5	Purple
Lysine.HCl	3	Purple
Methionine	1	Purple
Norleucine	0·4	Purple
Norvaline	0·5	Purple
Ornithine.HCl	3	Purple
Phenylalanine	5	Grey brown
Proline	1	Yellow
Serine	0·3	Brown red
Threonine	2	Pink purple
Tryptophan	2	Yellow brown
Tyrosine	3	Brown
Valine	0·2	Purple

results to be obtained, the paper should, however, be of an even structure and thickness; it should have some slight adsorptive properties and it should be completely free from contaminants which may, if present in more than trace amounts, lead to serious distortions or even to the production of double spots. For instance, when traces of copper are present in the paper the amino-acid spots when revealed with ninhydrin will have pink leading edges. These pink areas are due to the presence of a small amount of the copper salt of each of the amino acids. In the absence of any chelating agent in the solvent the copper salts are formed in increasing amounts as each amino acid spot moves down the paper. Very clean papers are, of course, specially desirable for quantitative work. Measurements of the ninhydrin colour obtained from the papers alone have shown Whatman Nos. 1 and 3 papers to be suitable for quantitative estimations of amino acids without any preliminary washing. For quantitative estimation of histidine, tyrosine and methionine, by the maximum colour density method, Schleicher and Schull 598, which is a specially even-textured paper, is recommended (Block *et al.*, 1958). Whatman No. 1 paper has excellent properties for most chromatographic purposes and is now widely used. Unless otherwise stated, this paper is suitable for the separations described in this book.

Since thicker papers allow heavier loading of the chromatogram, papers such as Whatman 3 MM are useful when more than approximately 0·5 mg of a complex mixture of amino acids are to be separated. When the same total loading is required, but fewer different species of amino acids are present, or if other substances help to make up the same total load, a thick paper will again be required.

Very heavy papers, especially if loosely textured, will give diffuse spots owing to very rapid solvent percolation. Fortunately, however, behaviour of this kind can be prevented if the solvent is fed into the thick paper via a piece of Whatman No. 1 a few inches wide. This is arranged as a bridge between the thick paper, on to which it is sewn, and the solvent reservoir. Whatman No. 54 paper has great mechanical strength even when wet with organic solvent and is therefore suitable for long chromatograms. An arrangement for the continuous removal of solvent from the bottom of normal length chromatograms is described on page 68. By this means long periods of development can be obtained without the formation of a pool of solvent on the lower part of the paper. The need for very long chromatograms can thus usually be avoided.

Solvents

Analar quality or redistilled solvents should always be used for chromatography because impurities originating from the solvent may interfere with spot detection. If the materials of which the spots are formed are to be eluted from the paper, the use of highly purified solvents is specially important. For reproducibility and to obtain expected R_f values, the ratios of all organic solvent or solvent and water mixtures must be closely controlled. For certain quantitative applications even the slight variation in the amount of water present, due to that which is introduced into the system as dampness in the filter paper, may be important. If chemical reaction can be expected to occur between the components of a solvent as, for instance, when esters are formed from acetic acid and alcohols, the length of time between the mixing and use of the solvent becomes important. Since such reactions are often faster in strong light these solvents are best kept away from illumination.

The following five solvents have been selected from the great many that have been used, because they make possible convenient separation of all amino acids and a large proportion of the lower peptides.

(1) *Butanol, Acetic Acid.* Equal volumes of water and n-butanol and 0·11 vol. of glacial acetic acid are shaken together. After separation the upper layer is ready to use for development of the chromatogram. The lower layer is placed in a separate shallow vessel in the chromatographic chamber. Since butanol, acetic acid is one of the more volatile solvents, saturation of the atmosphere in the chamber with water and solvent vapour is of great importance. For optimum results the paper, ready loaded with the spots of material for separation, should be in the box during this stage. When this procedure is used the chromatography is started after equilibration, by the addition of the organic solvent to the trough.

(2) *Phenol.* Four vol. redistilled phenol plus 1 vol. water plus 0·01 per cent 8-*HO*-quinoline. Freshly distilled colourless phenol should be saturated or partially saturated with water. After addition of 8-*HO*-quinoline the liquid should be stored in the dark. Alternatively, oxidation leading to colour formation may be slowed by occasionally bubbling coal gas through water-saturated phenol. Phenol in the absence of anti-oxidants and especially when used with ammonia, is subject to rapid oxidation and polymerization yielding increasing amounts of dark-brown substances; during chromatography this process which is catalysed by traces of metal must not be allowed to occur since characteristic finger-shaped irregularities at the solvent front are caused by polymerized phenol. A small volume of 1 per cent sodium cyanide solution placed in a separate container has a similar inhibitory effect and is often employed in addition to a chelating agent (e.g. ethylenediaminetetraacetic acid), which is dis-

solved in the phenol itself. Phenol may be used either completely saturated with water or when less than fully saturated. As might be expected, reproducible R_f values are more easily obtained with the fully saturated solvent.

(3) *Methanol, Water, Pyridine.* Eighty vol. methanol, 20 vol. water plus 4 vol. pyridine. Redistillation of methanol and pyridine is not usually necessary.

(4) *t-Butanol, Methylethyl Ketone, Water, Diethylamine.* Forty vol. t-butanol, 40 vol. methylethylketone, 20 vol. water plus 4 vol. diethylamine. Redistillation of solvents before use is not required but care must be taken to ensure complete removal of diethylamine from the chromatogram before spraying with ninhydrin. The process can be hastened by hanging the papers for 5 min. in an atmosphere of steam.

(5) *Collidine, Lutidine.* One hundred vol. each of redistilled 2,6-lutidine, 2,4,6-collidine and water plus 3 vol. diethylamine. Several mixtures of collidine, lutidine, water and diethylamine with sometimes the further addition of ethanol have been shown to yield satisfactory chromatograms. An alternative solvent mixture to the above, which has the advantage of being completely miscible with water and thus not subject to changes in composition at different temperatures, consists of 55 vol. 2,6-lutidine, 25 vol. ethanol, 20 vol. water and 2 vol. diethylamine. With more volatile mixtures such as this, temperature control and the degree of saturation of the chamber with solvent vapour become increasingly important. Collidine–lutidine solvent mixtures are convenient in that they are sufficiently stable to be kept for long periods at room temperature. Since the solubility coefficient of water in collidine is negative the preparation of a saturated solution is carried out below the required final temperature.

The R_f values of the commonly occurring amino acids in the solvents which have just been described, are given in Table 5.3. Under identical conditions of development of the chromatograms these values will be found to alter very little; however, as they are sensitive to such factors as temperature and degree of saturation with solvent vapour of the atmosphere in the chamber, they can be expected in practice to vary somewhat from run to run. Fortunately such variations always affect all the amino acid R_f values in a proportionate manner, thus the relative position of the spots will remain unaltered. Evidently identification of spots should always be carried out primarily by attention to relative R_f values.

Methods of Spot Detection

The positions occupied by spots consisting of amino acids and of peptides can be revealed most conveniently by means of the ninhydrin reaction. The spots of certain of the amino acids and peptides can also be detected by many other methods. In fact all the techniques listed in Table 5.1 have been used with success for the substances with which they react. Since, however, the ninhydrin reaction is both very sensitive and convenient, and because it can be adapted for quantitative work, only this method will be described in detail.

Ninhydrin Reaction, Detailed Technique. After completion of chromatography the solvent is removed from the paper either by evaporation at room temperature or in a drying oven (see page 71). The filter paper is then evenly sprayed with a solution of 0·5 per cent ninhydrin (for purification of ninhydrin cf. Block *et al.*, page 123) in n-butanol containing 10 per cent of water. Spraying is most easily carried out with the paper hanging in the vertical position. To prevent undue movement, weighted clips are attached at the lower edge. Some care is needed to ensure that the paper is wetted evenly with the ninhydrin solution; the degree of transparency reached will give considerable guidance. Since the free running of butanol containing 10 per cent of water over the paper is likely to cause some spreading and movement of those amino-acid spots with higher solubilities in this solvent, spraying should be stopped while the ninhydrin solution is still held stationary by the paper. Undoubtedly the spraying method is the simplest available and has the advantage that it is suitable for other colour reagents including those capable of dissolving the materials of which the spots themselves are formed; however, for those purposes where evenness of deposition of the ninhydrin is of first importance, and especially for quantitative investigations, the dipping method is to be recommended. This process is carried out most effectively by a single passage of the paper through the ninhydrin solution contained in a photographic dish or other flat vessel. The required solution should be diluted from a concentrated solution of ninhydrin in ethanol (cf. Quantitative Methods, page 111). After the application of ninhydrin, the damp paper is finally heated for 5 min in an oven at 100–105° C. As the solvent evaporates and the temperature of the paper rises, the separated amino acids become visible as spots which vary in colour from yellow to rose pink. The tints obtained with the majority of the amino acids vary only slightly so that identification by colour alone is not possible; however, these colour differences, when considered as additional evidence to that given by the positions of the spots, may be of considerable value. This is especially true if some degree of overlapping of the spots has taken place. The shades of colour given by the different amino acids are indicated in Table 5.2. The colour contrast can be greatly improved by the addition of 0·01 per cent of collidine to the ninhydrin solution. Unfortunately, however, even the bright green colour given by aspartic acid with this reagent is transitory, as continued heating of the chromatogram changes the colours of all the spots to an almost uniform pinkish-purple. The yellow colour due to proline is exceptional in that it is much more heat stable. The process of colour development can be most easily observed and stopped at the stage of optimum contrast when a glass-fronted oven is used (see page 71). For qualitative work some indication of the amount of each amino acid which can be expected to give a just visible spot may be of importance. These values are given in Table 5.2. Similar information in respect of two of the smaller peptides is also included. In general, the amount of colour given by the larger peptides is only a little greater (molecule for molecule) than it is for those containing few amino-acid residues.

Methods of Localization of Amino Acid and Peptide Spots other than by the Ninhydrin Reaction.

By conversion to N-chloro compounds and detection by means of the starch iodine reaction. This detection method makes use of tertiary butyl hypochlorite to convert substances containing peptide bonds to the corresponding *N*-chloro compounds. In practice the chromatogram is kept in the vapour of tertiary butyl hypochlorite for 1 h. The excess reagent is then removed by aeration for 6 h after which time the paper is sprayed with a 1 per cent solution of potassium iodide followed by a 1 per cent solution of soluble starch. Because iodine is liberated from potassium iodide by *N*-chloro derivatives, the spots appear as dark blue areas. This method which is due to Mazur, Ellis and Cammarata (1962) is sensitive enough to detect 0·1 μg of glycine. Rather larger amounts of most amino acids and peptides must be present to be detected, but the method is much more sensitive for peptides than is treatment with ninhydrin. In addition, spots containing as little as 5 μg of albumin can be detected.

By means of ultra-violet light. In the complete absence of ultra-violet absorbing residues from the solvents and if the paper is completely dry, the spots formed by all the amino acids appear in ultra-violet light as pale fluorescent areas. For this purpose a mercury arc lamp such as the Hanovia 'Homesun' 450W is required.

If phenol or other solvent with strong ultra-violet absorption has been used, the dry chromatogram should be washed several times with acetone and then thoroughly re-dried at a temperature of at least 150° C. Even under optimum conditions the sensitivity of this method is much less than that which is available using ninhydrin. Due to the strong ultra-violet absorption of tyrosine and tryptophan, the spots of these amino acids can be detected and conveniently recorded by the contact-printing photographic method described by Abelson (1960) (cf. page 117).

Detection of Radioactive Spots. Since all the amino acids can be obtained with carbon-14 or hydrogen-3 as constituent atoms, scanning and autoradiographic methods, if of sufficient sensitivity in relation to the available levels of radioactivity, are suitable for spot detection; furthermore, spots consisting of cystine, homocystine, or methionine, can be similarly localized when sulphur-35 is present. Substitution with iodine-131 permits the location of mono- and diiodotyrosine and thyroxine. Using carbon-14, a 5 μl spot containing 0·0001 μc is just detectable by autoradiography after an exposure of one week.

Quantitative Methods

Approximately Quantitative Estimations. Several single-dimensional chromatograms are developed using sufficient of the mixture undergoing analysis for the formation, after spraying with ninhydrin, of spots of medium intensity. Appropriate amounts of standard solutions containing the components of the mixture undergoing analysis (if known) are applied as a row of spots near one edge of a sheet of paper, alternately with spots of the solution to be analysed. The concentrations of the components of the standard solutions are so arranged that a row of standard spots is obtained, each of which is twice as strong as that immediately preceding it. This arrangement permits visual matching of known and unknown spots of suitably-spaced colour intensities. The most useful range of concentrations for such standards is 0·2–3·2 μg for each of the amino acids present. The accuracy of the results obtainable in this way can be increased by the adoption of any of the refinements to be mentioned below.

Quantitative Estimations; Maximum Accuracy, by the Maximum Colour Density Method. This method depends on direct measurement of the light absorbed by the spots on the chromatogram after colouration with ninhydrin. The photometer is adjusted so that the light passing through an uncoloured part of the paper at any point between the spots is taken as 100 per cent transmission. Detailed descriptions of both single- and two-dimensional methods based on this principle may be found in Block *et al.* (1958). They are stated to be the most accurate techniques available for the analysis of amino acids by means of paper chromatography. More recently, however, McEvoy-Bowe and Lugg (1961) have further improved the two-dimensional method and thus reduced the 'standard error of the mean' for triplicate assays to only 4·5 per cent. These improvements are incorporated in the description of the method given below. The single-dimensional method is of course considerably quicker and, because the standards can be included on the same sheet with the spots of the substances undergoing analysis, somewhat more accurate. With the apparatus of Datta, Dent and Harris, the standards for two-dimensional chromatograms are placed on sheets which are developed simultaneously by ascending chromatography in a single chamber. Phenol is used for the first dimension and is followed by the solvent mixture composed of lutidine, ethanol and water. For single-dimensional chromatography the appropriate solvent system is determined by the particular mixture of amino acids requiring separation. In Table 5.3 suitable solvents are given for the amino acids to be expected in hydrolysates of proteins.

Detailed Description of the Two-dimensional Method.

Apparatus. The arrangement shown in Fig. 3.19 is suitable. 12 sheets 20 × 20 cm. Whatman No. 1 or other suitable paper can be accommodated.

Sample application. Not more than 3 μl of each solution should be applied to the paper. If more is required the spot should be dried before each re-application. After application of the whole sample the paper is exposed briefly to ammonia vapour.

Standards. The less soluble amino acids are dissolved by addition of the minimum amount of hydrogen chloride, and isopropanol is added to a concentration of 10 per cent. Appropriate volumes of the

TABLE 5.3. R_f VALUES OF THE AMINO ACIDS IN THE SELECTED SOLVENTS

Amino Acids	*Solvents*				
	n-Butanol 1 Water 1 Acetic acid 0·11	Phenol	Methanol 80 Water 20 Pyridine 4	t-Butanol 40 Me Et Ketone 40 Water 20 Diethylamine 4	Collidine 100 Lutidine 100 Water 100 Diethylamine 3
Alanine	0·39	0·60	0·52	0·20	0·28
α-Amino butyric acid	—	0·77	—	—	0·21
Arginine	0·19	0·89	0·16	0·05	0·17
Asparagine	—	0·40	0·21	0·12	0·21
Aspartic acid	0·33	0·19	0·40	0·06	0·21
Cysteic acid	—	0·08	0·41	0·19	0·40
Cystine	0·17	—	0·18	0·06	—
Glutamic acid	0·37	0·31	0·48	0·06	0·20
Glutamine	—	0·57	0·31	0·10	0·22
Glycine	0·33	0·41	0·37	0·18	0·24
Histidine	0·19	0·69	0·28	0·18	0·27
Hydroxyproline	—	0·63	0·45	0·15	0·28
Isoleucine	0·68	0·84	0·68	0·45	0·45
Leucine	0·72	0·84	0·70	0·52	0·45
Lysine	0·18	0·81	0·15	0·10	0·11
Methionine	0·57	0·81	0·60	0·39	0·42
Norleucine	—	0·84	0·70	0·60	0·45
Ornithine	—	0·33	0·31	0·11	0·11
Phenylalanine	0·66	0·85	0·60	0·52	0·48
Proline	—	0·88	0·55	0·25	0·28
Serine	0·31	0·36	0·42	0·30	0·28
Threonine	0·36	0·50	0·50	0·50	0·34
Tryptophan	0·61	0·75	0·42	0·50	0·50
Tyrosine	0·53	0·51	0·50	0·30	0·51
Valine	0·56	0·78	0·65	0·35	0·36

standard solutions and those for analysis at concentrations of 2–8 μM/ml are then transferred to the papers. At least three replicate chromatograms of each standard and of each unknown should be prepared.

Hydration of the paper. Adequate hydration of the paper can be ensured either by brief exposure of the sheets to steam after they have been fixed in the frame, or alternatively, the solvent can be placed in the trough after a period of equilibration of the paper in the chamber with its lid in position. Large fluctuations of room temperature must be avoided. 20° C has proved to be a suitable temperature.

Solvents. First dimension. Water-saturated phenol containing in addition 10 per cent w/v phenol, 0·04 per cent w/v 8-*HO*-quinoline and 0·5 per cent w/v 2 : 6 lutidine. Second dimension. 55 vol. redistilled 2 : 6 lutidine plus 25 vol. 95 per cent ethanol plus 20 vol. water. 1·5 ml diethylamine is placed in a beaker at the bottom of the chamber.

Drying. The solvents should be removed at room temperature by means of a current of air which can be provided most easily from an electric fan. Complete removal of phenol is important and will require approximately 12 h.

Colouration with ninhydrin. The solution into which the sheets are dipped must be prepared freshly by dilution of 3 per cent ninhydrin in 95 per cent ethanol. This concentrated ninhydrin solution must be kept in the dark. To 5 vol. of the concentrated ninhydrin are added 5 vol. 95 per cent ethanol, 39 vol. redistilled chloroform plus 1 vol. 2 : 6 lutidine. The sheets are immersed for 2 s and then briefly dried in a strong current of air before the heating which is carried out for 30 min in an oven held at 90° C. Since the humidity is of great importance during colour development, damp air must be led into the oven at a fast rate (20 1./min). Suitable humidity and temperature of this air stream is obtained by bubbling it through slightly acidified water maintained at 43° C, followed by passage through a steam-jacketed condenser.

Photometry. After completion of colour development the sheets are kept in the dark. Photometry is then carried out within a few hours, using an instrument of the *minimum transmission type* (cf. page 72). Colour values are corrected by means of the transmittances given by the same sections of the chromatogram after each has been bleached with chlorine gas. The amounts of each amino acid originally present are then read off from the curves obtained by plotting the amounts originally taken for each standard spot against the average colour actually obtained, expressed as − log transmittance. Somewhat greater accuracy may be achieved by using a function α which is related to Transmittance (T) by the expression $(1/T) - 1 = \alpha$. McEvoy-Bowe and Lugg (1961) have shown that α, which can be taken as a measure of band colour, bears a linear relationship to the amounts of amino acid originally used. Full details regarding the application of this correction are given by McEvoy-Bowe and Lugg (1961) who show that the mean of triplicate assays of 5 amino acids is as reliable as the mean of 100 replicates under the conditions given originally by Block *et al.* (1955). To obtain this result (range of error

2·6–9·2 per cent with mean 4·5 per cent for s.e.m. of triplicates within each experiment), triplicate chromatograms each consisting of glycine, taurine, β-amino-iso-butyric acid, alanine and glutamine were developed simultaneously. There were seven experiments using 2 and 20 μm-mole and five experiments using 4 and 10 μm-mole quantities.

Conservation of Paper Chromatograms as such and Recording by Photography

The colours of spots formed from amino acids and ninhydrin disappear completely during the course of a few months. The rate of loss of colour can, however, be greatly retarded by spraying the coloured chromatogram with a dilute solution of cupric nitrate (1 ml saturated aqueous $Cu(NO_3)_2$ + 0·2 ml of 10 per cent HNO_3, diluted to 100 ml with ethanol). After neutralization of excess nitric acid with ammonia vapour the paper is dipped into a solution of Perspex in chloroform. For the permanent recording of chromatograms, however, photography is the most suitable method to use.

CARBOHYDRATES

Most of the common sugars can be separated by the same methods of paper chromatography as are used for the amino acids. In addition to phenol, collidine and n-butanol : acetic acid, which are all equally as effective for separation of sugars as they are for the amino acids, there are numerous specialized solvents. Three of these, together with the sugars for the separation of which they are suitable, are listed in Table 5.4. Removal of salt, prior to chromatography of the sugars, is of great importance. This can be done in any one of the three following ways.

(1) By extraction with pyridine. This should be carried out with the dry solvent at 100° C. There is some danger of epimerization.

(2) By ion exchange. A mixed resin such as Biodeminrolit may be used in batches. Alternatively two successive columns, using first a cation and then an anion exchanger, may be employed. Since the sugars are not ionized they are not retained by either of the resins.

(3) By electrolytic desalting, see page 68.

TABLE 5.4. SOLVENTS FOR PAPER CHROMATOGRAPHY OF SUGARS

Solvent Composition	*Sugars for which Solvent is suitable*	*R_f Values*
Ethyl acetate : pyridine : water 2 : 1 : 2 v/v	Xylose	0·38
	Arabinose	0·33
	Mannose	0·32
	Glucose	0·28
n-Butanol : pyridine : water 6 : 4 : 3 v/v	Lactose	0·31*
	Galactose	0·43*
	Glucose	0·48*
n-Butanol : pyridine : water 10 : 1 : 2 v/v	Oligosaccharides	—

* Measured on circular chromatograms.

TABLE 5.5. R_f VALUES OF SUGARS AND SUGAR DERIVATIVES

Compound	*Solvent System* *				
	1	2	3	4	5
D-Glucose	0·39	0·39	0·18	0·17	0·42
D-Galactose	0·44	0·34	0·16	0·14	0·36
D-Mannose	0·45	0·46	0·20	0·195	
L-Sorbose	0·42	0·40	0·20		
D-Fructose	0·51	0·42	0·23		0·47
D-Xylose	0·44	0·50	0·28	0·265	
D-Arabinose	0·54	0·43	0·21	0·22	0·45
D-Ribose	0·59	0·56	0·31		
L-Rhamnose	0·59	0·59	0·37	0·34	
Deoxy-D-'ribose'	0·73	0·60	—		
L-Fucose	0·63	0·44	0·27		
Lactose	0·38	0·24	0·09		
Maltose	0·36	0·32	0·11		
Sucrose	0·39	0·40	0·14		0·36
Raffinose	0·27	0·20	0·05		0·18

* Solvent systems given are: 1. Water-saturated phenol-1% ammonia-hydrocyanic acid. 2. Water-saturated s-collidine. 3. n-Butanol-acetic acid-water (4 : 1 : 5). 4. Ethyl acetate-acetic acid-water (3 : 1 : 3). 5. Amyl alcohol-n-propanol-water (4 : 1 : 15). In all cases the temperature was 20° C.

Based on a table from Kowkabany, G. N., *Advances in Carbohydrate Chem.* (1954), **9**, 303.

The R_f values of a number of sugars in the five most commonly used solvent mixtures are given in Table 5.5. Both the ascending and descending techniques can be used. Two-dimensional chromatograms are seldom necessary because the mixtures of sugars found in practice are not often very complex. Because of the very low R_f values of many of the oligosaccharides, repeated development is often required; alternatively, development by the continuous descending method may be used.

Colour Reagents

Numerous colour reagents for sugars have been described, and most of them belong to one of the following three different classes. An example from each of these classes will be described but should not be taken as being the most suitable reagent for any given mixture of sugars.

Oxidation Reagents. Much the most important of these is alkaline silver nitrate, the use of which was introduced by Partridge (1948), who first succeeded in separating sugars by means of paper chromatography.

Preparation and use of alkaline silver nitrate. A saturated aqueous solution of silver nitrate is diluted 200 times with acetone. Water is then added drop by drop until the precipitated silver nitrate is just redissolved. After drying, the chromatogram is passed quickly through this reagent and is then re-dried. When sprayed with 0·5N sodium hydroxide in aqueous ethanol, reducing sugars are revealed at room temperature as black spots. Some background colour due to excess silver oxide is formed by this method but this can be removed by washing the paper in water and then in a solution of sodium thiosulphate. 5N ammonia can be substituted for the 0·5N sodium hydroxide used in this reagent. If this is done, the reagent is made from equal volumes of 0·1N silver nitrate solution and 5N ammonia. The spots are revealed by heating the treated paper for 5–10 min in an oven at 105° C. Used thus the reagent becomes very unspecific; not only do sugars, alcohols, amino sugars, and glycosides react positively but so also do many non-carbohydrate substances. As little as 2 μg of the reducing sugars are revealed.

Aromatic Amino Salts. Although less sensitive than is silver nitrate, reagents containing these salts have the advantage that they give less background colour and fewer artifact spots.

Preparation and use of aniline phthalate reagent. 930 mg of aniline and 1·6 g phthalic acid are dissolved in 100 ml of water-saturated n-butanol. After spraying with this solution the paper is dried and heated to 105° C for 5 min. Brown and red spots are formed by a number of sugars. On the other hand, ketoses do not react. Fructose and uronic acid produce fluorescent spots. Sucrose reacts if the paper is heated more strongly, i.e. to 115–120° C for 10 min.

Phenolic Reagents. These are specially useful for the detection of ketoses. When phloroglucinol is used the pentoses give dark green spots and the aldohexoses light pink spots.

Preparation and use of naphthoresorcinol reagent. Equal volumes of 0·2 per cent naphthoresorcinol in ethanol and 2 per cent trichloroacetic acid in water are mixed. After spraying, the paper is heated to 105° C for 5 min. Blue-violet spots are formed by the aldopentoses. The reagent reacts particularly well with ketohexoses, yielding red spots. It is less sensitive than is the silver nitrate reagent.

PURINES, PYRIMIDINES AND THEIR DERIVATIVES

Once again, the general methods of paper chromatography suitable for separation of the amino acids are applicable. The following solvents can be used successfully for both groups of compounds: phenol, n-butanol : water, n-butanol : acetic acid and n-butanol : pyridine. If the nucleic acids have been hydrolysed to yield their constituent bases, adenine, guanine, uracil, thymine and cytosine in free form, a very wide range of solvents is available. This is because these basic substances are not readily attacked by either acids or alkalis. When, however, the bases are present as nucleosides or nucleotides or as the corresponding di- or tri-phosphates, strongly acid or alkaline solvents must be avoided or else breakdown by hydrolysis will take place. Four examples from the many available solvents are given (Table 5.6). All these solvents may be used for the ascending technique. Despite the sensitivity of the nucleotides towards acids, a very useful two-dimensional separation of some of these compounds and of the free bases can be made by means of isopropanol : hydrochloric acid followed by n-butanol : ammonia. Great care must be taken to avoid the presence of inorganic salts in the samples used for chromatography. This can be done either by starting with samples of nucleic acids which are themselves salt-free,

TABLE 5.6. SOLVENTS* FOR PAPER CHROMATOGRAPHY OF PURINE AND PYRIMIDINE BASES

Base	R_f Values			
	n-Butanol: NH_3 n-Butanol saturated with water at 23° C 100 ml 15 N.NH_4OH 1 ml	*n-Butanol: Formic Acid* n-Butanol 77 ml Water 13 ml Formic acid 10 ml	*Isopropanol: HCl* Isopropanol 170 ml Conc. HCl 41 ml Water 39 ml	*Isobutyric Acid: NH_3*† Isobutyric acid 400 ml Water 208 ml 25% NH_4OH 0·4 ml
Adenine	0·40	0·33	0·32	0·83
Guanine	0·15	0·13	0·22	0·70
Hypoxanthine	0·19	0·30	0·29	0·69
Xanthine	0·01	0·24	0·21	0·60
Uracil	0·33	0·39	0·66	0·67
Thymine	0·50	0·56	0·76	0·78
Cytosine	0·28	0·26	0·44	0·80
5-Me-Cytosine	0·36	—	0·52	—

* All of these solvents should be freshly prepared before use.
† This solvent is also suitable for the separation of nucleosides, nucleotides and the di- and triphosphates.

or by adsorption of the free bases on specially purified active charcoal. Elution from the charcoal is carried out either with 10 per cent aqueous pyridine or with ethanolic ammonia.

Location of Spots. Owing to their strong absorption of u.v. light, spots containing purines or pyrimidines can be easily revealed by examination of the dried paper in light from a lamp with high emission in the range 250–280 mμ (Markham and Smith, 1949). Suitable lamps include the Hanovia 'Homesun' mercury-arc lamp with maximum emission at 253·7 mμ. Two filters containing a cobalt sulphate-nickel sulphate solution, and gaseous chlorine, should be used in conjunction with this lamp. Alternatively, a Mazda mercury lamp may be used. When illuminated by either of these lamps, most purine and pyrimidine derivates will appear as dark spots showing up against the faint, light blue fluorescence of the paper. On the other hand, spots containing guanine and xanthine when the paper is slightly acid will fluoresce strongly, thus permitting differentiation from other purines and pyrimidines. If the spots seen in ultra-violet light are excised and eluted with acids or with ammonia, the amount of purine or pyrimidine compound in the eluates can easily be estimated quantitatively by spectrophotometric means. Alternatively, the filter paper containing the relevant areas can be passed through a spectrophotometer specially equipped for the purpose. If suitable standards are prepared at the same time this method will also give quantitative results.

Permanent records of such chromatograms can be made by laying the filter paper on a sheet of photographic paper such as Ilford 50M contact document paper, and exposing to ultra-violet light. Spots containing as little as 1 μg of the ultra-violet absorbing substance can be revealed and estimated by the above techniques. Optimum amounts for quantitative analysis of the purines and pyrimidines lie between 20–50 μg. Because of the ease with which purine and pyrimidine spots can be located and estimated by means of their ultra-violet absorption, the use of colour reagents for these substances is unnecessary. This is fortunate because no general colour reagent has yet been found which is sensitive and which will reveal all of these compounds. For these reasons only brief mention will be made of two specialized colour reagents.

Mercuric nitrate reagent for purines. The developed chromatogram is dried and then washed with ether. A solution of 0·25M mercuric nitrate in 0·5N nitric acid is sprayed on to the paper which is then dipped into aqueous ammonium sulphide. The spots thus formed from guanine, adenine, etc., are black.

p-Dimethylaminobenzaldehyde reagent for pyrimidines. The reagent consists of 1 g *p*-dimethylaminobenzaldehyde, 10 ml concentrated hydrochloric acid and 100 ml ethanol. After a preliminary light spray with 0·5N sodium hydroxide, the papers are sprayed with the reagent. After keeping for 2–6 h at room temperature the pyrimidines and their compounds appear as yellow spots.

REFERENCES

Abelson, D. (1960). *Nature, Lond.* **188,** 850.

Block, R. J., Durrum, E. L. and Zweig, G. (1958). *A Manual of Paper Chromatography and Paper Electrophoresis*, 2nd edn., Academic Press Inc., New York (1st edn., 1955).

Consden, R., Gordon, A. H. and Martin, A. J. P. (1944). *Biochem. J.* **38,** 224.

Katz, A. M., Dreyer, W. J. and Anfinsen, C. B. (1959). *J. biol. Chem.* **234,** 2897.

McEvoy-Bowe, E. and Lugg, J. W. H. (1961). *Biochem. J.* **80,** 616.

Markham, R. and Smith, J. D. (1949). *Biochem. J.* **45,** 294.
Mazur, R. H., Ellis, B. W. and Cammarata, P. S. (1962). *J. biol. Chem.* **237,** 1619.
Partridge, S. M. (1948). *Biochem. J.* **42,** 238.

CHAPTER 6

ION-EXCHANGE CHROMATOGRAPHY

PART 1. FEATURES OF ION-EXCHANGE RESINS

Ion-exchange consists essentially of a reversible exchange of ions between solid and liquid phases, without radical change occurring in the structure of the solid phase. The exchange properties of soils for various cations, which play an important part in plant nutrition, were discovered almost 100 years ago. Since then, natural clays, such as montmorillonite and fuller's earth, as well as synthetic alumino silicates have been used for investigations into the nature of ion-exchange and put to practical use for water softening. The last 25 years have seen the development of synthetic *ion-exchange resins* which consist of an inert, organic framework to which are attached ionizable groups, capable of participating in the exchange process.

Certain early resins, synthesized from phenol sulphonic acid and formaldehyde, or prepared by sulphonation of coal, contained ionizable hydroxyl and carboxyl groups in addition to the sulphonic acid groups intentionally introduced. This made their ion-exchange properties complex, so that resins of this type were less useful than they would have been if only a single type of ionizable group had been present. The development of the atomic bomb in the U.S.A. during the second world war gave rise to various problems involving the separation of groups of closely similar elements, such as the rare earths, some of which were present in very low concentrations. Such difficult separations were eventually achieved, having served as a stimulus for the synthesis of the monofunctional resins which today remain the most useful tools for ion-exchange chromatography. Well-known products of this type include the Amberlite, De-Acidite, Dowex and Zeo-Karb resins.

Structural Characteristics

Most ion-exchange resins in present day use have a framework or skeleton formed by the co-polymerization of the aromatic hydrocarbon styrene, with a smaller amount of divinylbenzene.

$$\underset{\text{styrene}}{\begin{array}{l}CH{=}CH_2\\ |\\ C_6H_5\end{array}} + \underset{\text{divinylbenzene}}{\begin{array}{l}CH{=}CH_2\\ |\\ C_6H_4\\ |\\ CH{=}CH_2\end{array}} \rightarrow \underset{\text{polystyrene (cross-linked with divinylbenzene)}}{\begin{array}{c}\begin{array}{ccccc}C_6H_5 & & & & C_6H_5\\ | & & & & |\\ -CH & -CH_2- & CH & -CH_2- & CH-CH_2-\\ & & | & & \\ C_6H_5 & & C_6H_4 & & C_6H_5\\ | & & | & & |\\ -CH & -CH_2- & CH & -CH_2- & CH-CH_2-\end{array}\end{array}}$$

If no divinylbenzene were present, long, unbranched chains of polystyrene would be formed. Each divinylbenzene unit introduced into the polymer becomes a point at which chain branching occurs. The degree of branching or cross-linkage of polystyrene chains thus increases with the proportion of divinylbenzene in the reaction mixture. The resulting polymer is insoluble, and has a porous open structure with an indefinitely large molecular weight (Fig. 6.1). This type of material has a high resistance to oxidation or reduction by chemical reagents and to physical attrition or breakage; it is also insoluble in most solvents. The branching of the chains introduces a third dimension into the structure, so that if hydrophilic groups are attached to the benzene nuclei and the polymer is treated with water, it swells up like a sponge, enclosing water molecules between the hydrocarbon chains. The *kind* of chemical behaviour shown by such a system depends on which ionizable groups are introduced into the benzene rings, but the properties of the inert framework can modify this behaviour in *degree*.

Another type of monofunctional ion-exchange resin in wide current use, which does not have a polystyrene matrix, is formed by polymerization of methacrylic acid and has free carboxyl groups

$$n\ \underset{\text{methacrylic acid}}{CH_2{=}\overset{\overset{CH_3}{|}}{C}{-}COOH} \rightarrow \underset{\text{polymethacrylic acid}}{-CH_2-\underset{\underset{COOH}{|}}{\overset{\overset{CH_3}{|}}{C}}-CH_2-\underset{\underset{COOH}{|}}{\overset{\overset{CH_3}{|}}{C}}-CH_2-\underset{\underset{COOH.}{|}}{\overset{\overset{CH_3}{|}}{C}}-}$$

Functional Groups

Ionizable groups, which retain their usual properties, and so give the resin its chemical characteristics, are firmly attached to the hydrocarbon skeleton by covalent bonds. These groupings are of two main types—acidic groups which give rise to resins with the properties of solid insoluble acids (*cation exchange resins or cation exchangers*) and basic groups on basic resins (*anion exchangers*).

Both the acid and base types of resin can be subdivided according to the strength of their ionizable groups. Strongly ionized acidic or

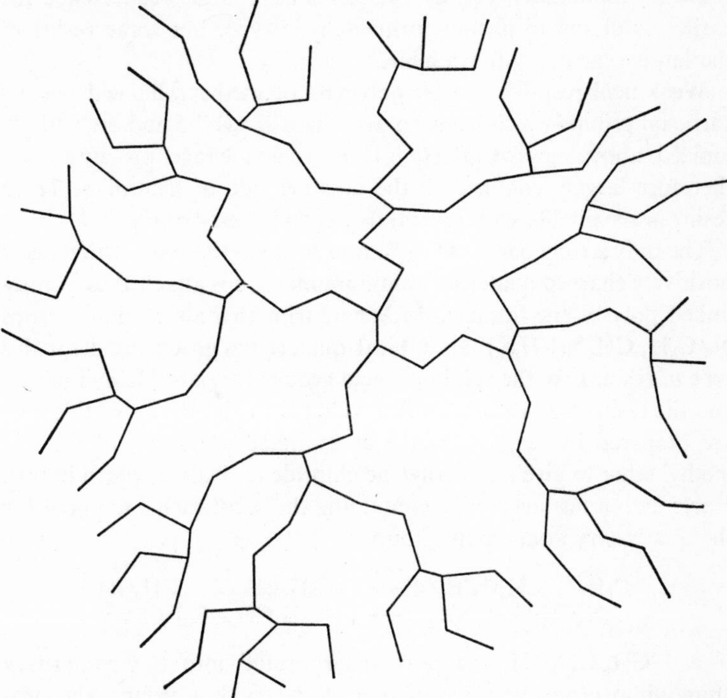

FIG. 6.1. Diagrammatic representation of a cross-linked resin. Only the backbone is shown, together with the cross-links (represented by the shorter lines). The three-dimensional lattice encloses spaces which can be penetrated by water and other small molecules.

basic groups, which are ionized over the greater part of the pH range 0–14, are present in *strong acid* and *strong base* resins respectively, and find useful application over a correspondingly wide pH range. *Weak acid* and *weak base* resins, however, are fully ionized only above and below pH 7 respectively, and their use is restricted to solutions in these parts of the pH scale. The chemical groupings which give rise to these four types of resin are described briefly below.

Of the strong-acid resins, those prepared by nuclear sulphonation of cross-linked polystyrene are most useful. The sulphonic acid groups are the only ionizable ones present. Moreover, both the acid and the salt forms are ionized over the entire pH range, so that the resin is effective at any pH. This type of resin has been widely used for the chromatography of amino acids, rare earths and many other substances. Sulphonated-polystyrene resins have largely superseded the earlier sulphonated-phenol–formaldehyde type, but some resins of the latter type are still available.

Weak acid resins based on polymers of methacrylic acid possess carboxyl groups which begin to dissociate at pH 3·5 and are entirely ionized above approximately pH 6. Ion-exchange properties are therefore largely confined to the alkaline side of neutrality. These resins are available with several degrees of cross-linking.

The only strong base resins of importance at the present time have positively charged quaternary ammonium groups attached to a cross-linked polystyrene framework. Benzyl trimethyl ammonium groups $[-C_6H_4.CH_2N(CH_3)_3]^+$ are typical quaternary groups used for this type of resin. Like the sulphonic acid groups they are highly ionized, and the resins may be used over a wide pH range. Resins of this type are prepared by reaction of the cross-linked polymer with chloromethyl ether to give a *p*-methylene chloride derivative, which in turn reacts with a tertiary amine containing the substituents required for the quaternary ammonium group

$$-C_6H_5 + CH_3OCH_2Cl \rightarrow -C_6H_4CH_2Cl + CH_3OH$$
$$-C_6H_4CH_2Cl + NR_3 \rightarrow [-C_6H_4CH_2NR_3]^+Cl^-.$$

If a $-CH_2.CH_2OH$ group is incorporated into the quaternary ammonium group in place of one of the methyl groups, the properties of the resin are slightly modified. It becomes a somewhat weaker base (though still in the strong-base class) and hence can be converted to the free-base form more efficiently. The modified resin is rather less stable at high temperatures.

Of the weaker basic resins, the tertiary amines with either diethylamino or dipropylamino groups attached to the benzene nuclei of the styrene-divinylbenzene co-polymer are probably the most useful. Another type, the polyamine resins, have a mixture of primary, secondary and tertiary amine groups on the polystyrene network. The effective range of the tertiary amine resins is approximately pH 0–9 and of the polyamine resins from pH 0–7. Some resins of the phenol–formaldehyde type with both amino and phenolic hydroxyl groups are still available. These resins are somewhat weaker bases than either of the types already described.

Commercial resins at present available in this country are classified in Table 6.1, which also gives details of their physical form, mesh-size and cross-linking.

Behaviour of Charged Groups on Resins

The charged groups of resins are invariably associated with ions of opposite charge so that electrical neutrality is maintained. These ions are held by electrostatic forces of attraction in the neighbourhood of the charged groups on the resin. They can be displaced, however, by other ions with charges of like sign. If the negatively charged sulphonic-acid groups of a resin are associated with hydrogen ions, the resin is said to be in the *hydrogen form*. Treatment with an excess of sodium chloride solution eventually replaces all the hydrogen ions by sodium ions, the resin thus being converted to the *sodium form*

$$R.SO_3^-H^+ + Na^+ + Cl^- \rightarrow R.SO_3^-Na^+ + H^+ + Cl^-.$$

In a similar way, the sodium ions might be replaced by other cationic species. Replacement of this type is the basis of chromatography on ion-exchange resins. It should be noted that the counter ion (chloride) plays no part in, and has little effect on, the changes taking place. This is characteristic of ion-exchange processes except where complex ion formation occurs.

Similarly, a basic resin in the hydroxide or free-base form is converted to the chloride form by treatment with sodium chloride solution

$$R.[C_6H_4CH_2N(CH_3)_3]^+OH^- + Na^+ + Cl^- \\ \rightarrow R.[C_6H_4CH_2N(CH_3)_3]^+Cl^- + Na^+ + OH^-.$$

Resins are supplied by the manufacturers in specified forms but can be converted easily to the most useful form for a particular chromatographic separation by treatment with an appropriate solution.

Exchange Capacity

The exchange capacity of a resin is a measure of the number of ionizable sites per unit of resin. The *total capacity* is the total number

TABLE 6.1. CHARACTERISTICS OF COMMERCIALLY AVAILABLE ION-EXCHANGE RESINS

Type	*Resin*	*Ionizable Groups*	*Matrix*	*Forms Available*	*Cross-linking**	*Mesh Sizes*	*Total Capacity†*
Strong Acid	Amberlite IR-120‡¶**	SO_3H	XPS	Na^+, H^+	9	A1	4·3
	Dowex 50‖	SO_3H	XPS	Na^+, H^+	1–16 (8)	D1	5·0
	Zeo-Karb 225§¶	SO_3H	XPS	Na^+	1–20	P1	5·0
	Zeo-Karb 215§	OH, SO_3H	PF			P2	—
Weak Acid	Amberlite IRC-50‡¶**	COOH	XMA	H^+		A1	10
	Zeo-Karb 226§¶	COOH	XMA	H^+	2·5, 4·5	P1	10
Strong Base	Amberlite IRA-400‡¶**	Quaternary ammonium	XPS	Cl^-	4	A2	3·3
	Amberlite IRA-401‡**	Quaternary ammonium	XPS	Cl^-	<2	A3	3·5
	Amberlite IRA-402‡	Quaternary ammonium	XPS	Cl^-	<2	A4	4·4
	De-Acidite FF§¶	Quaternary ammonium	XPS	Cl^-	2·5–8	P1	4·0
	Dowex 1‖	$[C_6H_4CH_2N.(Me)_3]^+$	XPS	Cl^-	1–10,16(8)	D1	3·5
	Dowex 21K‖	$[C_6H_4CH_2N.(Me)_3]^+$	XPS	Cl^-		D2	4·5
Fairly Strong Base	Amberlite IRA-410‡	Quaternary ammonium	XPS	Cl^-		A3	3·3
	De-Acidite H§¶	$>N(CH_3)^+$ (40% quaternary)	XPS	Cl^-	2·5–8	P1	3·8
	Dowex 2‖	$[C_6H_4.CH_2N(Me)_2C_2H_4OH]^+$	XPS	Cl^-	1–10(8)	D1	3·5
Weak Base	Amberlite IR-45‡¶**	$—N(C_3H_7)_2$	XPS	OH^-		A5	5·0
	De-Acidite G§¶	$—N(C_2H_5)_2$	XPS	Cl^-	2·5–8	P1	4·0
	De-Acidite J§	Polyamine (primary, secondary	XPS	Cl^-		P2	6·7
	Dowex 3‖	and tertiary)	XPS	OH^-	—	D3	5·5
	Amberlite IR-4B‡	Nuclear NH_2, —OH	PF	OH^-		A3	—
	De-Acidite E§	Nuclear NH_2, —OH	PF	Cl^-		P2	—

(See notes at foot of opposite page)

of ionized and ionizable sites per unit weight or volume. The *dry weight total capacity* is expressed in milligram equivalents per gram of the oven-dried resin, whereas the *wet volume total capacity*, which is smaller, is expressed per unit volume of swollen resin. The total capacity is the theoretical maximum which can ever be shown in any application, but the *operating capacity* is defined for a particular practical cycle, either in the above units or as a percentage of total capacity.

Particle Size

Resins manufactured by an emulsion–polymerization method have particles of nearly spherical shape known as *beads*. These have good hydraulic properties and offer a minimum resistance to the flow of liquids, settle in a minimum time and pack closely together when similar in size. In practice, resin beads range from 1 mm (1000 μ) downwards to about 10 μ which is the minimum useful size. Those larger than 1 mm diameter are unstable and crack easily, either during manufacture or in use, when subjected to excessive shrinkage and swelling. Small beads, of less than 300 μ diameter, are much more stable and are unlikely to fracture even after repeated cycles at extreme pH.

Bead resins should be used where larger particles are required (e.g. in de-ionization processes), since the spherical shape facilitates

---

* A range of values under cross-linking (%) indicates that a series of resins is available with intermediate values of cross-linking in addition to the extreme values stated. Those values given in brackets represent per cent cross-linking for the standard resins.

† Total capacity is stated in milli-equivalents per gram of dry resin.

‡ Amberlite resins are manufactured by the Rohm and Haas Company, Philadelphia, U.S.A.

§ De-Acidite and Zeo-Karb resins are manufactured by The Permutit Company Ltd, London, W.4.

|| Dowex resins are manufactured by the Dow Chemical Company, Midland, Michigan, U.S.A.

¶ Chromatographic grades of resin are available from British laboratory chemical suppliers. Amberlite chromatographic grades are designated by the prefix CG in place of IR or IRA.

** Analytical grades of resin are available from British laboratory chemical suppliers.

Key to Mesh Sizes Available (U.S. standard sieves unless otherwise stated)

A1 16–50, 100–200, 200–400, 400–600
A2 20–50, 100–200, 200–400
A3 20–50
A4 16–50
A5 16–50, 100–200, 200–400
D1 20–50, wet; 50–100, 100–200, 200–400, >400, dry
D2 16–20, 20–50, wet; 50–100, dry
D3 20–50, wet
P1 14–52, 52–100, 100–200, >200 (B.S. sieves)
P2 14–52 (B.S. sieves)

Key to Matrices

XPS denotes cross-linked polystyrene; PF denotes phenol-formaldehyde resin; XMA denotes cross-linked polymethacrylic acid.

rapid pouring of columns, backwashing and the mixing and separation of different resins. On the other hand, for chromatographic applications, which almost invariably require small particles ($< 160\ \mu$), good resolution can be obtained either with spherical or irregularly shaped particles. Suitable resin preparations for particular applications can be produced by grinding coarse resins in a hammer mill, followed by a fractionation for particle size either by sieving or sedimentation.

The particle size is usually stated by the manufacturer in terms of two standard sieves with mesh sizes such that the majority of the resin will pass through one but not the other. Some confusion has arisen because the size range of the parent polystyrene co-polymer, instead of the finished resin, has sometimes been given by the makers (Hamilton, 1958). Polystyrene itself is not wettable and the introduction of ionizable groups leads to swelling taking place on addition of water so that the final particle size can be double the original. For this reason, statements of particle size, to be meaningful, whether given in absolute units or in terms of sieve mesh, should refer specifically either to the original polymer or to the dry or swollen resin. The latter is clearly the most useful for chromatography. The form of the resin and the composition of the liquid phase should also be given. Particle sizes corresponding to appropriate British and American standard sieves are summarized in Table 6.2.

TABLE 6.2. APPROXIMATE SIZE OF OPENINGS IN BRITISH AND AMERICAN STANDARD SIEVES

Mesh or Sieve No.	*Size in Microns*	
	B.S.	U.S.
14	1200	1400
16	1000	1170
18	850	1000
20	—	840
22	700	—
50	—	300
52	300	—
100	150	150
200	75	75
300	53	—
400	—	38

Two different effects of particle size on solvent flow-rates for chromatographic separations must be carefully distinguished. First, the direct physical effect due to viscosity results in a diminution in the flow rate for a decrease in the size of the resin particles. This may also be expressed in terms of the increased pressure across the resin column necessary to maintain constant flow rate as particle size decreases. The second effect concerns the rate at which ionic equilibrium is established between a resin particle and the surrounding solution. Since reduction in particle size reduces the time for equilibrium to be reached, small particles allow faster rates of solvent flow for a given standard of sharpness of a chromatographic band. The kinetics of ion-exchange depend upon the times for diffusion of ions both from one resin particle to another and also inside each particle as well. The time required for the actual exchange of the ions associated with the charged groups on the resin is normally short compared with that required for diffusion, which consequently becomes the rate-controlling step. For high ionic concentrations, the rate of diffusion is inversely proportional to the square of the particle diameter, whereas for low concentrations the rate is inversely proportional to the diameter.

Fine resins are chromatographically more efficient than those composed of coarse particles, since they permit much faster flow rates for a given standard of band sharpness. Nevertheless, to obtain sufficiently fast flow-rates, increased pressure across the column will be needed to overcome the greater resistance to flow. Where the resin particles are very small, a pump may be necessary to increase the pressure. Reduction of particle size also increases the surface area per unit weight of resin and consequently results in an increased capacity for ionized molecules, such as proteins, which are too large to penetrate the interior of the particles.

Cross-linkage

As already mentioned, for resins with a polystyrene matrix, the amount of cross-linking depends primarily on the proportion of divinylbenzene present in the reaction mixture during the initial polymerization. The degree of cross-linkage is usually expressed as the percentage of divinylbenzene added (this is expressed as 'X numbers' for Dowex resins). Whereas the subsequent sulphonation step does not cause significant additional cross-linking, in the preparation of strongly acid resins, the chloromethylation step in the synthesis of basic resins, introduces methylene bridges between the hydrocarbon chains so causing additional cross-linking. Since these methylene bridges make a significant contribution to the total cross-linking of the resin, this cannot be accurately expressed, for basic resins, in terms of the proportion of divinylbenzene originally added.

The degree of cross-linking cannot be measured by chemical means on a given resin sample, but a comparative measure can be obtained in terms of the amount of water associated with the resin after it has been allowed to swell. The *water regain* is the weight of water which is associated with unit weight of the resin in a given form (usually sodium or chloride). In Table 6.3 the approximate corresponding

TABLE 6.3. COMPARATIVE VALUES OF WATER REGAIN AND CROSS-LINKAGE FOR PERMUTIT RESINS

Form	*Cross-linking %*	*Water Regain*
	1	6–12
Zeo-Karb 225	2	3–5
(sodium)	4·5	1·5–2·0
	8	0·9–1·1
	12	0·6–0·9
	20	0·4–0·6
Zeo-Karb 226	2·5	0·8–1·0
(hydrogen)	4·5	0·6–0·8
De-Acidites FF, G and H	2–3	1·5–2·0
(chloride)	3–5	1·0–1·5
	7–9	0·6–1·0

values of water regain and cross-linking, published by the Permutit Company for their resins, are given.

A *low* degree of cross-linking gives a resin an open structure with comparatively large spaces between the hydrocarbon chains. Such a resin will have a high permeability and can thus accommodate larger ions than a more highly cross-linked resin. At the same time, however, its selectivity for different ions is reduced. A highly permeable structure makes for rapid attainment of equilibrium and enables the resin to swell considerably. This gives such a resin a high moisture content, but reduces its physical stability and exchange capacity, expressed on a wet volume basis. Resins of *high* cross-linkage have smaller spaces between the neighbouring chains and consequently their properties are the reverse of those given for the lightly cross-linked resins. For polystyrene resins, 8 per cent can be regarded as an average degree of cross-linking.

Mechanism of ion-exchange Chromatography

Ion Exchange. The ionizable groups of strong acid and base resins form stable electrostatic bonds with ionized substances. Counter ions (i.e. ions of opposite charge to those exchanged by the resin) have little effect, but different ions of like charge can bring about displacement. For dilute solutions, the affinity for the resin increases with valency, while for related ions of the same valency it tends to increase with ionic radius. Lists in order of affinity have been compiled for both cations and anions. Monovalent metal ions show increasing affinity for strong acid resins as follows:

$$Li^+ < H^+ < Na^+ < K^+ < NH_4^+ < Rb^+ < Cs^+ < Tl^+ < Ag^+.$$

Divalent cations have the following order:

$$Be^{++} < Mg^{++} < Ca^{++} < Sr^{++} < Ba^{++}.$$

For monovalent anions on strong base resins, the affinities increase as follows:

$$F^- < OH^- < CH_3COO^- < HCO_3^- < Cl^- < NO_2^- < HSO_3^- = HSO_4^- < CN^- < Br^- < NO_3^- < I^- < CNS^-.$$

The increase of affinity with ionic size occurs only for ions which are sufficiently small to penetrate the resin network. Some ionized (organic) molecules are too large or are sterically unsuited to enter the interior of the resin easily and the capacity of the resin for these ions is correspondingly reduced.

Various chromatographic techniques make use of the primary ion-exchange property of resins. In *elution* methods, the resin is initially equilibrated with the eluant so that both are in the same ionic form, and in equilibrium. The mixture of substances is placed on the column, and on continued elution, they gradually pass down the column as a series of zones which slowly spread out. In *displacement* analysis the displacing agent either has a more strongly adsorbed ion than that initially attached to the resin or a much higher concentration of the same ion. The displaced substances pass down the column as zones which do not spread out. *Complex-ion* methods depend on washing the column with a solution of an ion of opposite charge which forms a stable complex with the ion to be separated. This reduces the effective concentration of the free ion in solution and so removes it from the resin. Solutions containing citrate, which forms complex-ions with lanthanum, have been used to remove this element from acid resins in the hydrogen form, and so separate it from other rare earths.

Methods for Controlling the Rates of Movement of Substances on Ion-exchange Columns

Of the various factors which influence the rates of movement of substances in ion-exchange chromatography, three can be adjusted easily in order to obtain optimum separations.

(1) The concentration of the ion of opposite charge to the resin.
(2) The pH of the eluting solution.
(3) The temperature.

Proper initial selection of these variables largely determines the efficiency of a particular separation. In addition, changes may be made during the course of elution so that optimum conditions are maintained for the separation of those substances which are very strongly held by the resin. The variables may be altered separately or simultaneously, the changes being made either in steps or continuously (i.e. gradient elution).

Usually the resin column is equilibrated with the solution that is to be used to start the elution, before the sample to be separated is added. The type of ion opposite in charge to the groups on the resin determines the *form* of the resin (see page 123) and the concentration of this ion has a profound effect on the rate of movement of the substances being separated (which have a charge of like sign). Increase in the concentration of this ion, increases the rate of movement of the substances undergoing chromatography, since an effect of the *mass-action* type leads to displacement from the resin to the moving phase. Examples of the use of ionic concentration to control separations are described later in this chapter in relation to particular classes of compound, e.g. the elution of arginine at neutral pH from a sulphonic-acid resin by increasing the sodium-ion concentration. It should be noted that where the resin is in the hydrogen form, changes in the concentration of acids used for elution may operate by this displacement effect, without significant alteration in the state of charge of substances undergoing separation. This type of mechanism predominates in the elution of amino acids and amino sugars from sulphonic-acid resins by hydrochloric acid.

If changes in the pH of the eluting solution are made in a region where the state of ionization of the substance undergoing separation is altered, a second method of control becomes possible. Different substances will be affected to different degrees in this respect, for a given change in pH. An example of this type of control is found in the elution of amino acids from sulphonate resin by means of citrate buffers of closely controlled pH, within the range pH 3–7.

Increase in temperature reduces the time necessary for the establishment of equilibrium between resin and moving phase. At higher temperatures the flow rate of the column can be increased somewhat without broadening of the peaks and consequent loss of resolution. Changes in the pH of the eluant and in the ionization constants of the substances being separated, both of which are temperature dependent, may influence relative rates of movement. This has been found for two pairs of amino acids—glutamic acid and proline; tyrosine and phenylalanine.

PART 2. PRACTICAL PROCEDURES WITH RESINS

Storage and Rehydration

Powdered resins supplied in dry form can be stored as such. Moist bead resins, however, should not be allowed to dry out as this may cause fracture of the beads. To prevent drying, the resin should be kept in tightly stoppered bottles or in sealed polythene bags. If, inadvertently, drying occurs, the beads should be wetted first with saturated sodium chloride solution, which can then be replaced gradually by distilled water. Handling and initial wetting of dry powdered resins should be carried out in a fume cupboard to prevent the particles being inhaled.

Preliminary Treatment

Standard grades of resin, as usually supplied, need a preliminary treatment to remove fine particles and soluble impurities. This treatment also conditions the resin before it is actually used for chromatography. The resin is first stirred in a large volume of water to break up any clumps of particles, so forming a suspension which is then allowed to stand for a suitable time, according to the particle size, after which the supernatant liquid together with the 'fines' is drawn off by means of tubing attached to a tap pump. The resin is again suspended in more water, allowed to settle, and the fines removed, the process being repeated until the supernatant liquid is clear. The resin is then transferred to a column and put through a number of alternate depletion and regeneration cycles. Solutions of 5–10 per cent hydrochloric acid and sodium hydroxide are suitable for strong acid and strong base resins, the resin being washed with water after both acid and alkali treatments. For weak acid and weak base resins, the concentrations should be 1–5 per cent; exceeding the upper limit may result in fracture of the resin particles. With sulphonated polystyrene resin of fine particle size, it is advisable to treat with 4 per cent sodium hydroxide solution at 40–100° C for some hours (Moore and Stein, 1951) although this treatment is likely to produce further fines. These fines should be removed by decantation and the treatment with hot alkali repeated until the supernatant liquid remains clear.

During the initial treatment with acid and alkali, and during the first few regeneration cycles, coloured material may be leached out of the resin. This is not detrimental to the resin, but represents a desirable removal of impurities.

Some manufacturers supply a more expensive grade of resin, termed 'analytical', which is ready for immediate use as the preliminary treatment with acid and alkali, initial regeneration, and washing have already been carried out.

Fractionation for and Measurement of Particle Size

For chromatography, the particle size of the resin should be reasonably small, preferably below 150 μ in diameter, and should fall within a narrow range. A moderately efficient method of particle fractionation can be carried out by the method of *wet sieving*. The resin, which has been given its preliminary treatment, is suspended in the solution with which it is to be eluted in the column, and is poured on to the coarser of the two sieves which are to determine the range of particle size (Table 6.2). The resin remaining on the sieve is washed with more of the same solution until no more resin comes through. The washings are carefully collected, poured on to the finer sieve and again washed with the solution. The resin remaining on this sieve is now suitable for chromatography.

Hamilton (1958) introduced a very elegant back-washing technique for the grading of resin particles into different size ranges, which permits closer fractionation and is applicable to smaller particles than the wet-sieving method. The resin to be fractionated is placed in a conical (Squibbs type) separating funnel (Fig. 6.2) which is filled with water. A stream of distilled water, which has been freed from air bubbles, enters the separating funnel at the lower tap and passes out of a tube connected to the top of the funnel. The presence of resin in the bottom of the funnel prevents axial streaming of the water, which at low-flow rates moves uniformly across all horizontal planes in the funnel. The velocity of flow gradually decreases as the widest part of the funnel is approached and then increases again as the funnel narrows towards the top. Particles of any given size will tend to remain stationary at some definite level in the lower part of the funnel so that their falling velocity, as determined by Stokes' law, is equal to the linear velocity of the rising liquid. Larger particles will remain near the bottom of the funnel whereas the average size will decrease at higher levels. For a given rate of water flow, there will be a particle diameter which corresponds to the velocity at the widest part of the funnel. Particles of this size will eventually be carried out at the top, since the vertical velocity increases above the widest part of the funnel.

The apparatus starts operating at a slow, but constant, flow rate and the liquid passing out is collected in a large container. When the emerging liquid is clear, the flow rate is increased slightly to another constant rate, and the effluent is collected in a second vessel. In this way, a series of fractions of gradually increasing particle size can be obtained. Hamilton found that the method was equally satisfactory for resins with spherical or irregularly shaped particles.

Measuring the size of resin particles can be done quite easily with a microscope, either directly, i.e. by means of a calibrated eyepiece micrometer or by photomicrography at known magnification, when the images of the particles may be measured with a ruler. A fairly large number of particles distributed among several fields should be measured in this way to give an average value for the diameter. For spherical particles, measurement of diameters presents no difficulty.

The size of irregularly shaped particles may be defined in terms of *Martin's* (or *accidental*) *diameter* which is equal to the length, *measured in a fixed direction across the microscope field*, of the longest

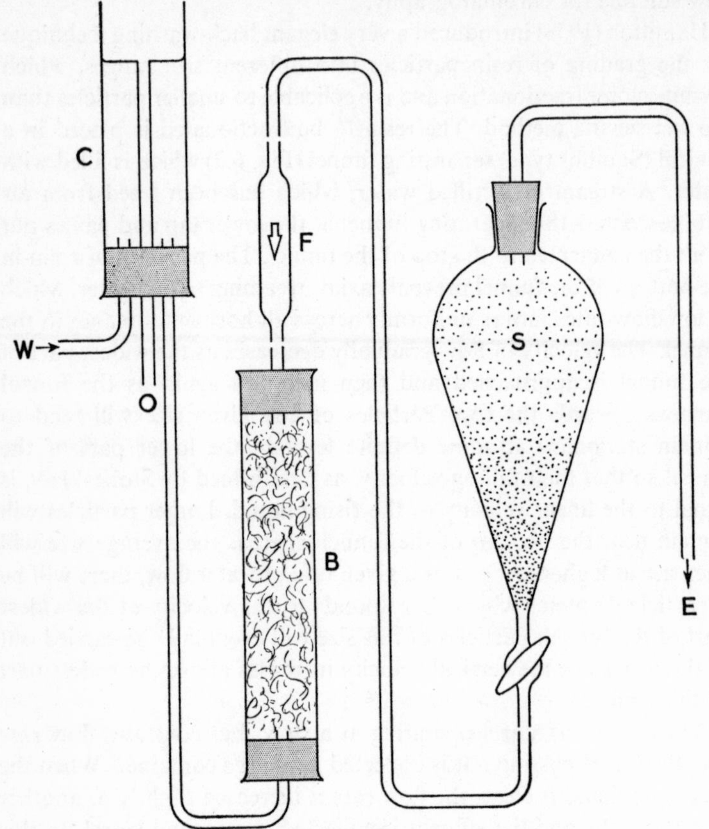

FIG. 6.2. Apparatus for fractionation of resins by particle size.
W Inlet for distilled water.
C Constant-level device.
O Overflow.
B Bubble trap filled with glass wool.
F flow meter.
S Separating funnel containing resin in suspension.
E Exit for resin suspension.

line, which bisects the area of the particle. This is not the actual length of the line itself but of its projection on to a fixed 'horizontal' line, the direction of which is determined by the eyepiece micrometer. The arithmetical mean of these accidental diameters is a useful representation of particle size.

Packing Columns with Resin

Columns are most easily packed by pouring in a carefully stirred suspension or slurry of the resin in water or buffer solution. The suspension of resin is then allowed to settle with the column placed vertically. The particles sink through the liquid until they come to rest on the support at the bottom of the column. At the same time, the liquid runs through the mass of resin particles and out at the bottom of the column. During settling, a certain amount of reclassification of resin particles takes place, the largest tending to sink to the bottom while the smallest settle at or near the top of the resin bed. This effect will not cause irregularity of flow provided that there is uniform distribution of particles in all horizontal planes, with only random variations. Reclassification is most marked when a thin suspension of resin is poured into the column; for example, one which, when left to stand, gives approximately equal volumes of settled resin and supernatant liquid. With a thicker suspension, particles of different sizes tend to remain mixed, but the suspension may be difficult to pour unless it is kept well stirred. It is essential to ensure that air bubbles do not become trapped between the resin particles while the column is being poured. Long narrow columns are best poured in several stages, giving rise to sections of approximately equal length. If each new section is poured while 3 to 4 in. of liquid remain above the surface of the section which has just settled, the latter will not be disturbed.

Precautions with Resin

In certain circumstances resins can undergo large percentage changes in volume, which may be sufficient to shatter the glass tube in which they are contained; therefore a column should not be packed with dry resin before water is added. Similar considerations apply when the liquid surrounding the resin has to be changed, e.g. from an organic solvent to water.

Formation of air pockets in a column may cause channelling of liquid or even complete cessation of flow. This applies particularly when a column is run above room temperature, in which case the liquid phase should be de-gassed before use, either by boiling or by means of a vacuum pump.

If any of the solutions added to the top of the column contain finely divided suspended matter, this will collect on top of the resin and may eventually block the column. Thin layers of such debris are usually easily removed with a Pasteur pipette without disturbing the resin.

Measurement of Water Regain

The resin is allowed to swell in the solution in which it is to be used for chromatography. It is then transferred to a sintered-glass funnel and either attached to a vacuum pump for 10 min or, preferably, is placed in a centrifuge and run at a speed equivalent to a force of 20 g for 5 min. The moist resin particles are quickly transferred to a weighing bottle, weighed, dried overnight at 110° C and again weighed. The ratio of the loss of weight on drying to the weight of the dry resin is the water regain, and forms a practical measurement of the degree of cross-linking. Some manufacturers publish tables or graphs relating these two variables for individual resins (Table 6.3).

PART 3. SEPARATIONS USING ION-EXCHANGE RESINS

Amino Acids

Ion-exchange chromatography is particularly suitable for the separation of amino acids since these compounds contain at least two ionizable groups per molecule. Partridge and his co-workers (1949–1951) devised methods for separating a variety of organic acids and bases, amino acids and related compounds by displacement chromatography on cation- and anion-exchange resins. Elution chromatography, mainly on cation-exchange resins, has been developed by Stein, Moore and co-workers (1950–58) into a versatile tool for the separation of complex mixtures of amino acids from protein hydrolysates and biological fluids. The elution technique has subsequently been used more widely than displacement chromatography. This is due to its wide application as an analytical method. It is well suited for this purpose because complete separation of amino acids emerging successively from the column can be easily obtained. In addition, by making small adjustments to the composition of the eluting solutions, the relative positions of neighbouring peaks can be controlled.

Stein and Moore (1950) first separated amino acids on columns of the sulphonated polystyrene type resin, Dowex 50, by elution with increasing concentrations of hydrochloric acid (1·5–4N). The amino acids were eluted exclusively in their cationic forms by the substantial concentration of hydrogen ions provided by the hydrochloric acid. As the hydrogen ion concentration increased so did the eluting power of the solvent, the following equilibrium being displaced in the downward direction:

$$\text{Resin } C_6H_4SO_3^- \ldots\ldots NH_3^+\text{—}\overset{\text{H}}{\underset{\text{R}}{\text{C}}}\text{—COOH} + H^+ + Cl^-$$

$$\rightleftharpoons$$

$$\text{Resin } C_6H_4SO_3H + NH_3^+\text{—}\overset{\text{H}}{\underset{\text{R}}{\text{C}}}\text{—COOH} + Cl^-.$$

This method has not been used a great deal, because during the following year Moore and Stein (1951) developed a more elegant way of separating amino acids on sulphonic acid resin by means of a series of buffers of increasing pH in the range pH 3–7. Between pH 1 and pH 3 the amino acids, being almost exclusively in their cationic forms, are strongly held by the negatively charged groups on the resin. Above approximately pH 3 the α-carboxyl groups begin to ionize so that the molecule passes from the cation to the 'zwitterion' form. Since the latter has a net charge of zero, it is not electrostatically attracted to the resin. As the pH increases, the following equilibrium is displaced downwards so that the ratio of the zwitterions to cations

$$\text{Resin } C_6H_4SO_3^- \ldots\ldots NH_3^+\text{—}\overset{\text{H}}{\underset{\text{R}}{\text{C}}}\text{—COOH} + Na^+ + Ci^-$$

$$\text{pH 3–7} \quad \rightleftharpoons$$

$$\text{Resin } C_6H_4SO_3^-Na^+ + NH_3^+\text{—}\overset{\text{H}}{\underset{\text{R}}{\text{C}}}\text{—COO}^- + H^+ + Ci^-$$

increases, resulting in the rapid movement of the amino acid down the column.

By careful selection of precise pH and sodium-ion concentration of the buffer, it is possible to control the relative rates of movement of the different amino acids. Moore and Stein (1951) separated all the neutral and acidic amino acids normally found in protein hydrolysates on columns of Dowex 50, 100 cm high, using two citrate buffers both 0·2N with respect to sodium, and having pH values of 3·42 and 4·25 respectively (Fig. 6.3). The pH of the first buffer is especially critical since a variation of $\pm$ 0·05 unit causes the cystine peak to coincide either with alanine or valine. After prolonged elution with the first buffer, the amino acid peaks begin to lose their sharpness and become more attenuated (e.g. valine) but changing to the buffer of higher pH restores sharpness to the remaining peaks (methionine, isoleucine, etc., see Fig. 6.3).

The basic amino acids have an additional positively-charged group on the side chain, R, which tends to maintain the molecules in cationic form. For this reason, buffers of relatively high pH are required for the elution of basic amino acids from the 100-cm column by the following type of mechanism:

$$\text{Resin } C_6H_4SO_3^- \;....\; NH_3^+\text{—}\underset{\underset{R^+}{|}}{\overset{\overset{H}{|}}{C}}\text{—}COO^- + Na^+ + A^-$$

$$\text{pH 6–11} \quad \Big\updownarrow$$

$$\text{Resin } C_6H_4SO_3^-Na^+ + NH_3^+\text{—}\underset{\underset{R}{|}}{\overset{\overset{H}{|}}{C}}\text{—}COO^- \quad \begin{bmatrix}\text{histidine}\\ \text{hydroxylysine}\\ \text{or lysine}\end{bmatrix}$$

$$\text{or} \quad + NH_2\text{—}\underset{\underset{R^+}{|}}{\overset{\overset{H}{|}}{C}}\text{—}COO^- + HA$$

[arginine]

Exposure to high pH causes partial decomposition of the basic amino acids on the columns so that quantitative recoveries are not obtained. They may, however, be separated without loss (Moore and Stein, 1951) on a shorter (15 cm) Dowex 50 column under milder conditions, with a 0·1M sodium phosphate buffer, pH 6·8, followed by

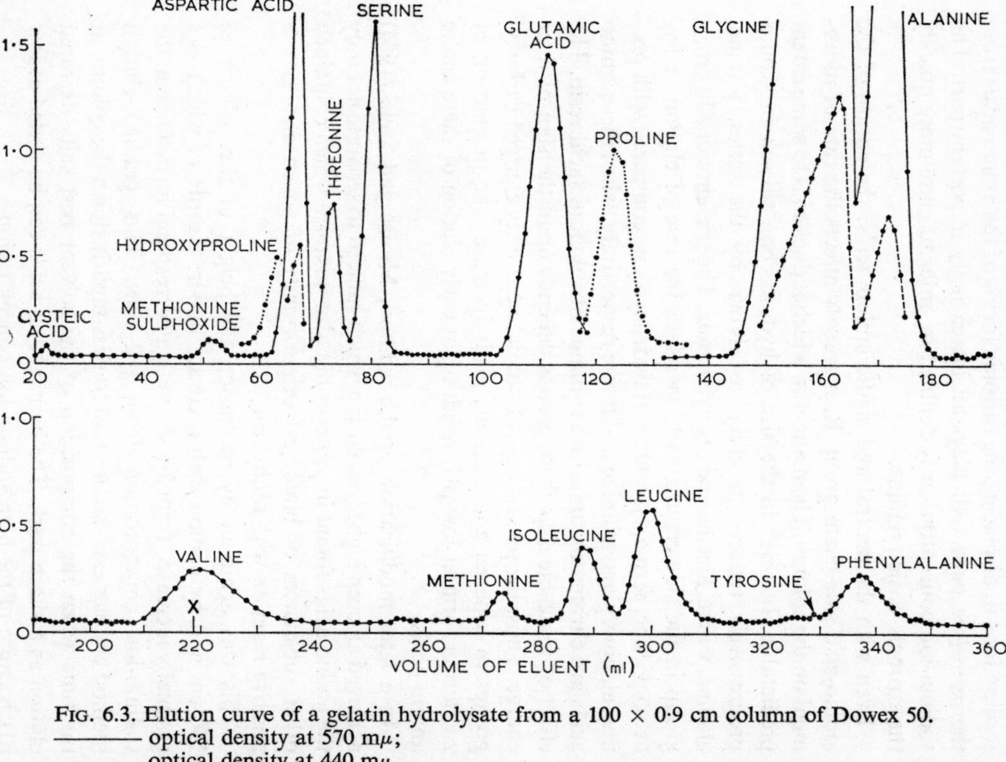

FIG. 6.3. Elution curve of a gelatin hydrolysate from a 100 × 0·9 cm column of Dowex 50.
——— optical density at 570 mμ;
.... optical density at 440 mμ.
Buffer changed from pH 3·42 to 4·25 at point X. (Eastoe, J. E., 1955, *Biochem. J.* **61**, 595).

a 0·2M sodium citrate buffer of pH 6·5 (Fig. 6.4). At these low pH values, the mechanism given above probably predominates for histidine, but occurs only to a limited extent for hydroxylysine and lysine and not at all for arginine. On the other hand, the effect of sodium ions in displacing the cationic forms of the amino acids from the resin (see page 130) plays an increasingly important part. The sodium-ion concentration is doubled in order to elute more quickly the strongly basic arginine.

Even with the neutral and acidic amino acids, the nature of the amino-acid side chain group R, markedly affects the rate of movement on the column. The manner in which it does so is to some extent predictable. Increase in the size of hydrocarbon side-chain groups progressively reduces mobility, as shown by the series, glycine, alanine, valine, leucine and phenylalanine. The presence of a hydroxy group in the side chain greatly increases the rate of elution of hydroxyproline, serine, tyrosine and hydroxylysine compared with proline, alanine, phenylalanine and lysine respectively, when these amino acids are chromatographed on columns of sulphonic-acid resin. The effect of ionizable side-chain groups depends upon the sign of their charge. Thus, the presence of additional negatively charged carboxyl groups in aspartic and glutamic acids increases the proportion of zwitterion form at low pH, resulting in early elution of these acidic amino acids.

In a later modification of the method, Moore and Stein (1954) achieved an even higher resolution which sufficed to separate not only the amino acids found in proteins but also mixtures which contained other substances of biological origin, many of which also give a positive reaction with ninhydrin.

This was achieved by increasing the height of the column to 150 cm and by eluting with a citrate buffer, the pH of which was gradually increased from 3·1–5·1 with a corresponding increase in the sodium-ion concentration from 0·2–1·4N. This gradient-elution method enables each amino acid to pass rapidly down the column at the time when the composition of the solvent best suits its rapid elution as a sharp peak. The basic amino acids can be eluted at low pH because of the high sodium-ion concentration.

The methods described above necessitate the manual analysis of 600–850 separate fractions collected over a period of seven days. This is both tedious and time-consuming for the operator. Fractionation of resin particles according to size (Hamilton, 1958) enables

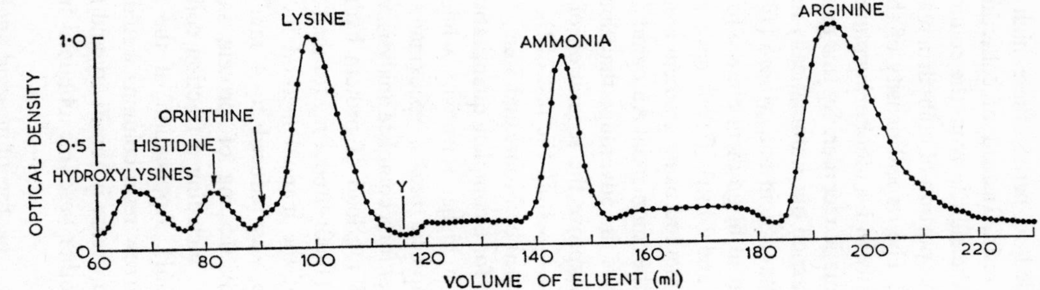

FIG. 6.4. Elution curve of a gelatin hydrolysate from a 15 × 0·9 cm. column of Dowex 50. Buffer changed from pH 6·75, 0·1M sodium phosphate to pH 6·5, 0·2M sodium citrate at the point marked Y. (Eastoe, J. E., 1955. *Biochem. J.* **61**, 595.)

columns to be made from resin with very fine particles of relatively uniform size distribution. Such columns permit much faster flow rates with maintenance of sharp peaks, so that it is possible to carry out a complete analysis in 24 h (Moore, Spackman and Stein, 1958). Very high pressures are needed to permit these high flow rates through the columns of fine resin. Instead of collecting separate fractions for manual analysis, the effluent from the column is mixed continuously with the correct proportion of ninhydrin reagent and is passed through a heating coil. The optical density of the resulting solution is measured continuously with a monitoring photometer and plotted as a graph by an automatic recorder. By this means a complete protein analysis can be carried out automatically in 24 h. For the sake of simplicity, Spackman, Stein and Moore (1958) used a stepwise elution by buffers instead of gradient elution for the automatic method. Recently, Piez and Morris (1960) have published a modification of the automatic method using gradient elution with a complex gradient produced by the commercial Autograd device. This provides high resolution and has the advantage that 'local' adjustments can be made easily to improve the separation of particular groups of amino acids, without upsetting the rest of the elution.

The manual technique developed by Moore and Stein (1951) needs only 5–10 mg of protein sample for a complete quantitative analysis. The automatic methods have a higher sensitivity while retaining accuracy for the smaller amino-acid peaks. Spackman, Stein and Moore (1958) have suggested that for a complete analysis, when using their automatic technique, a 3 mg load of protein hydrolysate is suitable, while Piez and Morris (1960) used 1 mg for their technique. A scaled-down modification of the manual method in which the diameter of the resin column was reduced to 4 mm has been developed, which requires only 0·5 mg of protein sample and standard laboratory equipment, including a fraction collector and spectrophotometer (Eastoe, 1961). Application of the automatic method in conjunction with narrow resin columns would probably provide a considerable further increase in sensitivity and some gain in accuracy, owing to the smoother base line obtained in a closed system.

The variety of techniques available for amino-acid analysis using ion-exchange resins makes it extremely difficult to choose the one which is most suitable for a particular investigation and laboratory. The manual methods use simple and comparatively inexpensive equipment, but require much more time per analysis, whereas the automatic techniques need considerable expenditure on, or ingenuity in, the construction of apparatus, but enable an analysis to be carried out in a single day with rather smaller samples, and at best, some gain in accuracy over the manual method. In large research institutes where analysis of many samples is required, one of the automatic methods may be established with advantage as a standardized technique; on the other hand, the investigator working alone and requiring analyses of comparatively few samples, will probably find the manual method more suitable.

Whatever technique is chosen, it is essential to adhere closely to the many details of the published procedure until the method is set up and experience is gained in its use. Insufficient space is available in this book to give experimental details of any of the published methods, but some of their main features are summarized in Table 6.4 which may assist in the selection of a suitable modification. Some aspects which appear to be critical for the successful setting up of an accurate procedure are discussed briefly as follows.

The *buffer solutions* should be prepared in large quantities (e.g. 10 l.) so that after standardization there is sufficient for many analyses. Addition of thymol (0·25 g/l.) will prevent growth of moulds, and storage in borosilicate glass enables a constant pH to be maintained for periods up to at least 2 yr. The buffer solutions should be prepared from carefully weighed quantities of reagents, batches of which are specially reserved, and the pH adjusted to the correct value using a glass electrode and a pH-meter, reading to approx. ± 0·02 unit. It is advisable to have all solutions at 25° C for these measurements and to use 0·05M potassium hydrogen phthalate (pH 4·00 at 25° C) as the primary standard. The functioning of the glass electrode and pH-meter may be checked, using a 0·05M borax solution in boiled distilled water (pH 9·17 at 25° C). Substances such as thiodiglycol, benzyl alcohol, ethylenediaminetetra-acetate and detergents are best added to smaller portions of the buffer solution when required for chromatography and need not be present when the pH is adjusted. When a fraction collector of the drop-counting type is used, the concentrations of both thymol and detergent should be standardized, as they affect surface tension and hence the size of drops and fractions.

The *ion-exchange resin* itself is probably the most critical material, affecting resolution and separation of amino-acid mixtures. Different investigators have obtained good results with Dowex 50, Amberlite

TABLE 6.4. CHARACTERISTICS OF PUBLISHED PROCEDURES FOR AMINO-ACID ANALYSIS BY RESIN CHROMATOGRAPHY

Reference	*Technique*	*Resin*	*Columns* (length × dia.)	*Buffers*	*Temperature* °C	*Load* (mg)	*Time for Analysis*	*Accuracy* %
Moore and Stein (1951)	Manual	Dowex 50 8% cross-linked 200–400 mesh	100 × 0·9 cm* 15 × 0·9 cm†	pH 3·42 and 4·25 citrate* pH 5·0 citrate† pH 6·8 phosphate† pH 6·5 citrate†	37, 50, 75 25	2 × (3–5)	4+3 days	±3
Moore and Stein (1954)	Manual	Dowex 50 4% cross-linked§	150 × 0·9 cm‡	Citrate with gradient elution pH 3·1 ⟶ 5·1 [Na+] 0·2 ⟶ 1·4N	30, 50, 75	2·5	7 days	±3
Spackman, Stein and Moore (1958)	Automatic	Amberlite IR-120 8% cross-linked 40 μ* 25–30 μ†	150 × 0·9 cm* 15 × 0·9 cm.†	pH 3·25 and 4·25 citrate* pH 5·28 citrate†	50 50	2+1	17+5 hours	±3
Piez and Morris (1960)	Automatic	Dowex 50 12% cross-linked 25–32 μ	133 × 0·9 cm.‡	Citrate with Autograd elution pH 2·9 ⟶ 7·2 [Na+] 0·25 ⟶ 2·4	60	1	24 hours	At least ±3 At best ±1
Eastoe (1961)	Manual	Dowex 50 12% cross-linked 200–400 mesh	100 × 0·4 cm.* 15 × 0·4 cm.†	pH 3·42 and 4·25 citrate* pH 5·0 citrate† pH 6·75 phosphate† pH 6·5 citrate†	37, 65 25	0·5	4+3 days	±5

* For acidic and neutral amino acids. † For basic amino acids. ‡ For all amino acids. § Poured afresh for each run.

IR-120 and Zeo-Karb 225, and no definite differences have been established between them. Disappointing results have, however, been obtained by some workers owing to inconstancy of different batches of the same resin even when designated by the manufacturer as being the same percentage cross-linking and particle size range. Experience shows that these properties are best checked by the user (see pages 133 and 136) and further supplies obtained when a batch proves unsuitable. Even with this precaution, the final test is the separation obtained on the column, and if this is inadequate, the suitability of the resin should be suspect and another batch tried. Some adjustment of the relative positions of the amino acids which emerge in the early part of the run is possible by altering the temperature or buffer pH, but such compromises would not be necessary if consistent batches of standard resins were available. For separations using the manual method with suitable resin (generally of the bead type), it is sufficient to clean the resin by alternate treatments with sodium hydroxide and hydrochloric acid solutions as well as removal of large particles by wet sieving, and fines by sedimentation. For practical details see Moore and Stein (1951). For the automatic method, resin of smaller particle size is required and suitable homogeneous fractions are most readily prepared by the hydraulic back-washing method of Hamilton (1958). Both ground and bead resins have been used successfully for the automatic method. Some workers claim that columns of the bead type retain more constant flow-rates over a long period of use.

Amino acid standards for colorimetric calibration and for checking recovery should be selected carefully and tested for purity. In a collaborative assay to compare the accuracy obtainable in different laboratories, difficulty was experienced due to substantial proportions of impurities in several amino acids obtained in this country (Bender *et al.*, 1959). Glycine is possibly a better primary standard than leucine, which was originally suggested, since its high solubility facilitates preparation of standard solutions.

Sugars

Before the development of chromatography, the separation of sugar mixtures was formidably difficult. Neutral sugars behave as non-electrolytes under most conditions and consequently have little affinity for ion-exchange resins. At very high pH values, however, the hydroxyl groups become ionized and the resulting negatively charged sugar molecule can be adsorbed by strong-base resins in the hydroxide form. Sugars are slowly eluted when a column of such resin is washed with water but are more rapidly displaced by a sodium chloride solution, which converts the resin to the chloride form. Sugar alcohols, unlike sugars themselves, have no affinity for basic resins and can be eluted rapidly with water. Unfortunately, chromatography on strong base resins in the hydroxide form is of very limited value for separating sugars, which under sufficiently strongly alkaline conditions are unstable and may undergo isomerization (e.g. glucose to fructose and mannose) or decomposition to products such as lactic or glycollic acids.

A more useful technique for sugar chromatography on anion-exchange resins makes use of their initial conversion to borate complexes, Khym and Zill (1951). These complexes are formed when polyhydroxy compounds with pairs of *cis*-hydroxyl groups react with borate ions:

$$\begin{matrix}=C-OH\\ |\\ =C-OH\end{matrix} + H_3BO_3 \rightleftharpoons \left[\begin{matrix}=C-O\\ |\\ =C-O\end{matrix}\!\!>\!B\!<\!\!\begin{matrix}OH\\ \\ OH\end{matrix}\right]^- H^+ + H_2O \qquad (1)$$

monodiol boric acid

$$\left[\begin{matrix}=C-O\\ |\\ =C-O\end{matrix}\!\!>\!B\!<\!\!\begin{matrix}OH\\ \\ OH\end{matrix}\right]^- H^+ \rightleftharpoons \begin{matrix}=C-O\\ |\\ =C-O\end{matrix}\!\!>\!B-OH + H_2O \qquad (2)$$

$$\left[\begin{matrix}=C-O\\ |\\ =C-O\end{matrix}\!\!>\!B\!<\!\!\begin{matrix}OH\\ \\ OH\end{matrix}\right]^- H^+ + \begin{matrix}=C-OH\\ |\\ =C-OH\end{matrix} \rightleftharpoons \left[\begin{matrix}=C-O\\ |\\ =C-O\end{matrix}\!\!>\!B\!<\!\!\begin{matrix}O-C=\\ |\\ O-C=\end{matrix}\right]^- H^+ + 2H_2O \qquad (3)$$

bis diol boric acid (spirane)

Sugars readily undergo such reactions in aqueous solution at room temperature, equilibrium usually being reached in less than 5 min. The three types of complex are probably in equilibrium, the position of which depends on the type of sugar, the pH, and the concentrations of sugar and borate. When the concentration of sugar is low, relative to borate, the monodiol boric acid predominates for the monosaccharides. For disaccharides the uncharged molecule shown in equation (2) may be the dominant form. The negatively charged borate complex ions are well suited for chromatography on anion-exchange resins. By having the resin in the borate form and eluting with borate solutions, the equilibria are weighted to favour complex formation. A high pH minimizes the total borate concentration required and the range pH 8–9 has proved suitable for chromatography but is not so high as to cause decomposition of the sugars.

By using a selection of low concentrations of potassium tetraborate, sometimes with the addition of boric acid to reduce the pH, it is possible to separate a wide range of sugars and sugar alcohols (Table 6.5). Separations may be achieved on 11 × 0·9 cm columns of 200–400 mesh Dowex 1 resin, using a loading of 5–10 mg of each sugar, and flow rates of 0·5–1 ml/min. Initially the resin should be freed from fines, washed with N hydrochloric acid, converted to the borate form with 0·1M potassium tetraborate, then washed with water to remove excess borate, and finally equilibrated with the dilute borate solution selected for the elution.

Quantitative recovery of sugars is possible after separation of the borate complexes. The method is of wide application; disaccharides can be separated from monosaccharides and the individual components of hexose and pentose mixtures resolved. Sometimes it is necessary to alter the composition of the eluting buffer to achieve separation, thus mannose and fructose run together in 0·016M potassium tetraborate but the mannose can be eluted first in a buffer of lower pH (Table 6.5). Several structural factors affect the positions of the sugar–sugar borate equilibria and also the affinity between the resin and the borate complexes. Such factors include mutarotation and furanose–pyranose interconversion, and while these do not permit a complete explanation of the behaviour of sugar borates on columns, certain generalizations can be made. For non-reducing sugars, the affinity for the resin increases with molecular weight so that the di-, tri- and tetrasaccharides, sucrose, raffinose and stachyose are eluted in that order. Introduction of a functional group markedly increases the affinity; fructose for example is eluted after the oligosaccharides, though it is of lower molecular weight.

The progress of the elution of sugars can be readily followed by colorimetric analysis. If both the anthrone reagent of Dreywood (1946) and the orcinol method (Brown, 1946) are applied to the eluate, the positions and sizes of both pentose and hexose peaks may be assessed. It is also possible to isolate pure sugars from the borate-buffer solution. Thus passage through a column of a sulphonic acid resin in the hydrogen form yields a boric acid solution of the sugar. This is evaporated almost to dryness on a vacuum rotary evaporator and a large excess of pure methanol is added. The solution is again evaporated to small volume. This causes boric acid to be removed as the volatile methyl borate. Addition of methanol and evaporation is repeated twice to remove the last traces of borate. The residue of sugar is then dissolved in water, the solution filtered and crystallization induced by the usual methods.

TABLE 6.5. CONDITIONS FOR THE SEPARATION OF SUGARS AS BORATE COMPLEXES ON COLUMNS OF DOWEX 1. ANION-EXCHANGE RESIN

Type of Sugar	*Eluting Solution*	*Sugars in Order of Elution*
Hexoses	(i) 0·016M $K_2B_4O_7$	(Fructose and mannose), galactose
	(ii) 0·03M $K_2B_4O_7$	Glucose
	(i) 0·05M H_3BO_3 + 0·004M $K_2B_4O_7$	Mannose
	(ii) 0·015M $K_2B_4O_7$	Fructose
Pentoses	(i) 0·08M H_3BO_3 + 0·004M $K_2B_4O_7$	Ribose, arabinose
	(ii) 0·03M $K_2B_4O_7$	Xylose
Hexoses and pentoses	(i) 0·015M $K_2B_4O_7$	Ribose, fructose, arabinose, galactose, xylose
	(ii) 0·03M $K_2B_4O_7$	Glucose
Disaccharides	0·005M $K_2B_4O_7$	Sucrose, trehalose, cellobiose, maltose, lactose, melibiose
Partial hydrolysate of a disaccharide	(i) 0·005M $K_2B_4O_7$	Sucrose
	(ii) 0·02M $K_2B_4O_7$	Fructose
	(iii) 0·03M $K_2B_4O_7$	Glucose
Monosaccharides and oligosaccharides	(i) 0·005M $K_2B_4O_7$	Raffinose
	(ii) 0·015M $K_2B_4O_7$	Rhamnose, stachyose, sorbose, gentiobiose, melibiose
Sugar alcohols	(i) 0·015M $K_2B_4O_7$	Sorbitol, dulcitol
	(ii) 0·03M $K_2B_4O_7$	Mannitol

Ion-exchange chromatography of the borate complexes of sugars offers a useful method for separating larger quantities than is possible on paper chromatograms. The main disadvantage of the column method is the comparatively large volume of buffer solution needed to achieve separations. For this reason the duration of such experiments may be unduly long. Recovery of small amounts of separated sugars from large volumes of solutions is also necessary.

Acidic Sugar Derivatives

A number of sugar derivatives possess one or more acidic groupings which make it possible to carry out chromatography of these compounds on anion-exchange resins. The uronic acids are found in several animal polysaccharides of high-molecular weight together with basic amino sugars. The uronic acids resemble their parent sugars in structure except that C–6 is part of a carboxyl group instead of carrying a primary alcohol. This carboxyl group is rather unstable, the molecule being decarboxylated by hot acid. The two most common members of this group, glucuronic and galacturonic acids may be separated on anion-exchangers (e.g. Dowex 1 and Amberlite IR–4B in the acetate form). The oligosaccharides of galacturonic acid as far as the tetrasaccharide have been separated on Dowex 3 formate, while seven distinct oligosaccharides resulting from enzymic hydrolysis of hyaluronic acid have been separated on Dowex 1 formate. Their identification has helped to show that hyaluronic acid is a polymer with alternating glucuronic acid and glucosamine units.

The sugar phosphates are important metabolic intermediates concerned with the supply of energy for biosynthesis. Although the phosphate groups are strongly acidic, good separations of mixtures of sugar phosphates do not result from eluting them from anion-exchange resins with dilute acids, presumably because of the strongly hydrophilic nature of the sugar molecules. Better resolution is obtained by making use of borate-complex formation. Potassium tetraborate is incorporated in the slightly alkaline ammonia–ammonium chloride buffers used to elute the sugar phosphates from columns of Dowex 1 resin in the chloride form. Glucose-1-phosphate, glucose-6-phosphate and ribose-5-phosphate may each be eluted separately by gradually reducing the borate concentration. Adenosine mono- and diphosphates, fructose-1, 6-diphosphate and adenosine triphosphate are finally removed from the column in that order by very dilute hydrochloric acid (Khym and Cohn, 1953).

The isomeric 2-, 3-, and 5-phosphates of ribose may be eluted successively from Dowex 1 resin in the chloride form with a dilute solution of ammonium chloride and potassium tetraborate. The addition of borate affects the position of the 3-phosphate only, as the other two compounds do not form complexes.

Amino Sugars

The naturally occurring amino sugars are mostly aldohexoses which have the hydroxy group of C–2 replaced by an amino group (hexosamines). These hydrophilic bases with several hydroxy groups may be readily separated from one another by ion-exchange chromatography. Strongly acid (sulphonated polystyrene) resins, eluted with dilute hydrochloric acid solutions, have been most widely used. Thus Gardell (1953) resolved mixtures of the two most common amino sugars, glucosamine and galactosamine, on Dowex 50 columns, using 0·3N hydrochloric acid. More recently, Crumpton (1959) compared the behaviour of eleven substances of this class on columns of Zeo-Karb 225 resin eluted with 0·33N hydrochloric acid. Most of these substances could be separated from one another and it was shown that the '$R_{glucosamine}$' values, which ranged from 0·71–1·94, provide a useful means of identifying unknown amino sugars in conjunction with the results from paper chromatography.

Glucosamine and galactosamine appear as individual peaks during the course of standard ion-exchange chromatography of the amino acids; however, their positions of emergence from the 100-cm columns do not appear to be reproducible (see Partridge and Davis, 1955), perhaps due to small variations of resin, pH and temperature. These substances may, however, be completely separated from one another and from all the amino acids normally found in acid hydrolysates of proteins, on a 15-cm column of Dowex 50 with 0·1M sodium phosphate buffer of pH 6·75. Since these amino sugars react quantitatively with ninhydrin to produce a purple colour, the quantities present in hydrolysates of mucoproteins and mucopolysaccharides are readily determined (Eastoe, 1954).

The Rare-earth Elements

Ion-exchange chromatography is just as effective for the separation of inorganic ions as it is for ionized organic substances. One of the most striking advances made in this field is the complete separation of the rare-earth elements. These form a group of fifteen elements whose properties are closely similar, since their orbital configurations differ only in the gradual filling-up of one of the *inner* shells. The elements occur as mixtures of oxides in certain minerals, only very small proportions of some of them being present. The very similar properties of these elements render them difficult to separate from each other. Classical methods of separation which depended on repeated crystallizations of the most suitable salts were extremely tedious.

The entire group of rare-earth metals can now be separated on an analytical scale in quantities down to 100 μg of each element by ion-exchange chromatography (Ketelle and Boyd, 1947, 1951). The technique used in some ways resembles that already described for amino acid mixtures. Separation is carried out on long, narrow columns (97 × 0·5 cm) of a sulphonic acid cation-exchange resin (e.g. Dowex 50) of small particle size (270–375 mesh). The column is eluted with a series of ammonium citrate buffers, the closely controlled pH of which is increased by small steps (pH 3·20, 3·33, 3·40) during the course of the run. A high temperature (100° C), maintained by a steam jacket around the column, permits rapid attainment of equilibrium. A fairly fast flow rate is used, 2 ml/min/cm^2 of column cross-sectional area, compared with 0·1–0·6 ml/min/cm^2 for amino acid chromatography. The elution may be followed most readily by radioactivation methods, the mixture being initially bombarded with neutrons before it is put on the column and the radioactivity of the eluate is continuously recorded to give a series of peaks. The rare-earth elements leave the column in exactly the reverse order of their atomic numbers from lutetium (atomic no. 71) to cerium (atomic no. 58). In this way separations are completed in a few days which would otherwise take several years of work to achieve.

The use of citrate is especially important in rare-earth chromatography, since it forms complexes with the rare-earth ions, whereas in amino acid separations, this anion acts simply as a convenient buffer. With the rare earths, the primary function of complex formation is to reduce the effective concentration of simple metal ions in solution and *not* to convert an uncharged molecule into a charged complex suitable for ion-exchange, as occurs with the borate complexes of the sugars.

Further advantages in using citrate as a complex-forming agent are: the effective increase in the capacity of the column and the possibility of using a higher flow rate, due to the relatively small proportion of the total rare earth which is associated with the resin.

Another feature is that the position of the equilibrium between the metal ions and their citrate complexes is determined by both citrate concentration and pH, since the latter will affect the extent of dissociation of citric acid. These two factors will, in turn, control the distribution of rare earth between solution and resin and hence the rate of movement of the zones relative to that of the moving phase. Increase in the citrate concentration will lead to more rapid elution of rare earths.

For analytical purposes, a high citrate concentration (4·75 per cent hydrated citric acid) is employed, together with a low column loading and a low pH, from 3·2–3·4 (Ketelle and Boyd, 1947). In larger scale separations, the citrate concentration is reduced for economic reasons, and the pH increased in order to compensate for the reduction in the rate of movement of the rare earths, which would otherwise occur. Rare earths can be prepared in 100-g quantities using columns 10 cm in diameter and up to 2·5 m in height (Spedding, 1949). The use of large column loadings and low citrate concentrations results in considerable overlap of adjacent peaks in the initial chromatogram. This makes it necessary to carry out repeated separations on fractions containing two rare earths, which can eventually be obtained in 99·9 per cent pure form. On a preparative scale this re-fractionation procedure has proved more economical than a single run under the high resolution conditions (low column loading, high temperature, high citrate content) of the analytical method, since one operator can attend to a number of columns.

Peptides

The behaviour of peptides on ion-exchange columns is basically the same as that of their constituent amino acids, and similar methods have been used for their chromatographic separation on resins. The lower chemical stability of peptides needs to be considered, however, when selecting the conditions for chromatography, since high temperatures or exposure to strongly-acid solutions may result in hydrolysis. The main differences which affect the chromatography of peptides compared with amino acids, are the larger size of the individual molecules and the greater number of molecular species which may occur.

The molecules of many peptides are of the same order of size as the pore spaces between the hydrocarbon chains of the resin. In order that the peptide molecules shall freely penetrate the resin, the pore spaces must be sufficiently large. As already described (see page 128) pore size increases with reduction in the degree of cross-linking. Moore and Stein (1951) found that Dowex 50 resin with 8 per cent cross-linking was suitable for dipeptides, while for somewhat larger peptides, such as leucylleucylglycylglycine, sharper peaks were obtained with 4 per cent cross-linked resin. Piez and Saroff (1961) recommend the use of 2 per cent cross-linked material for the larger peptides having more than about ten residues. They also point out, however, that columns of such lightly cross-linked resin may shrink by as much as one third of their original length, due to changes in the ionic strength of the buffer during the course of elution.

The large number of possible peptides usually prevents the identification of individual ones from their position in the elution diagram. Instead, it is necessary to isolate each substance after separation and then to determine its amino acid composition and sequence. For this latter purpose, the buffer salts used for chromatography must be removed. This may be done either by 'desalting' or, more conveniently, by using suitably volatile substances, such as ammonium formate and ammonium acetate.

Separation of peptide mixtures is more often required in connection with studies on protein structure, especially the amino-acid sequence, rather than for the investigation of natural mixtures containing peptides. The protein is subjected to a partial hydrolysis by a suitable method, chosen to give the simplest possible mixture of peptides. The peptides and amino acids can then be separated by ion-exchange chromatography either completely or into groups which can be further resolved by chromatography using modified conditions.

Moore and Stein (1951) showed that peptides can be separated on columns of the sulphonated polystyrene resin Dowex 50, using the series of citrate buffers (pH 3·4, 4·2) which they originally developed for amino acid separation. Conditions for the efficient separation of simple peptide mixtures encountered in transamidation studies were systematically investigated by Dowmont and Fruton (1952) for Dowex 50 in 30 $\times$ 0·9 cm columns. Sodium citrate buffers ranging from pH 4·0–5·5 at a temperature of 30° C, with fairly slow flow rates (2–3·5 ml/h) were found to be suitable. These conditions have since been widely adopted for the separation of peptides. The eluate fractions, which were analysed by the ninhydrin method of Moore and Stein (1948) contained a range of di-, tri- and tetrapeptides giving 0·70–1·65 times the colour yield of an equimolar quantity of leucine.

The peak positions, characteristic of 25 peptides eluted by specified single buffers, were found to be largely independent of the flow rate of the buffer. The peptide peaks were usually quite sharp when resin of 8 per cent cross-linking was used, except for those peptides containing aromatic or leucine residues, which gave much broader peaks. Sharp peaks, and consequently much better separations of the latter type of peptide (e.g. glycyl-L-leucyl-L-leucine) can be obtained on 4 per cent cross-linked resin. Certain generalizations can be made concerning the rates of movement of peptides. Those composed of a *single* amino acid always emerge after that amino acid, whereas dipeptides with two *different* amino acids emerge *after both* amino acids. Brenner and Burckhardt (1951) have shown that tripeptides generally emerge after the corresponding dipeptides, though long side chains (e.g. leucine) also increase adsorption, sometimes even more than an additional peptide bond; thus leucyl glycine is more strongly adsorbed than triglycine.

Schroeder, Honnen and Green (1953) obtained a partial hydrolysate of gelatin by treatment with 3·6N hydrochloric acid at 37° C for seven days, and subjected it to chromatography on 8 per cent cross-linked Dowex 50. A preliminary separation into a number of peptide zones was achieved on a 100-cm column, but resolution was sufficient for the direct isolation of only one peptide in a state sufficiently pure for identification. The mixtures from the remaining zones were converted to dinitrophenyl peptides, which were then separated by partition chromatography on Celite columns. The separation of the complex mixture of 'random' peptides obtained by partial hydrolysis of a protein with acid was thus shown to be difficult to accomplish in a single step. More encouraging results have been obtained after preliminary enzymic hydrolysis which, under favourable circumstances, can be specific for particular bonds in the protein. Hirs, Moore and Stein (1956) hydrolysed ribonuclease, a protein of 126 residues, with trypsin, after preliminary oxidation with performic acid to break the disulphide bonds. This enzyme is reasonably specific for the peptide bonds formed from the carboxyl groups of lysine and arginine residues. It was possible to achieve 50–100 per cent yields for 13 peptides on Dowex 50 resin of 2 per cent cross-linking. Long columns (150 cm) were used to obtain sufficiently high resolution, and they had a diameter of 0·9 cm for analytical and exploratory work and 1·8 cm for isolation studies. Gradient elution was employed, using the same buffer systems previously developed for amino acid analysis (Moore and Stein, 1954). The lightly cross-linked resin permitted satisfactory separation of peptides ranging in size from 2–22 residues. All these peptides were subjected to amino-acid analysis after complete hydrolysis. Hirs, Stein and Moore (1956) continued working on these lines, using pepsin and chymotrypsin which have specificities for different peptide bonds, and were able eventually to formulate a structural formula for the amino acid sequence of ribonuclease.

A recent valuable contribution to problems of peptide separation has been the application of the anion-exchange resin Dowex 1, of 2 per cent cross-linking, in the acetate form, in conjunction with volatile bases (Rudloff and Braunitzer, 1961). Collidine (p*K* 7·45) and pyridine (p*K* 5·23) permit the preparation of buffers with acetic acid which have a pH in the region of the p*K* of the terminal amino group of peptides (approx. 8·0); furthermore, these volatile bases do not react with ninhydrin, and therefore permit direct colorimetric analyses of peptides in the eluates. Isolation of peptides is possible by removing the buffer solution on a rotary evaporator (Partridge, 1951). A logarithmic pH gradient is achieved by gradual addition of buffers containing, first, 0·1N acetic acid, second, 2N acetic acid and finally, by addition of the pure acid. This method has proved very useful in working out the structure of the globin from human haemoglobin-A. Piez and Saroff (1961) consider that the methods based on Dowex 1 will prove at least as useful as those previously established with Dowex 50, since with the former it is possible to isolate peptides having over 100 residues.

Proteins

Although ion-exchange chromatography would appear from theoretical considerations to be an ideal method for the separation of macromolecular polyelectrolytes, the work of a number of investigators suggests that it cannot be so widely nor so easily applied to proteins as it is to smaller molecules. Nevertheless, mixtures of certain closely similar proteins have been successfully separated on ion-exchange resins, the carboxyl type of weakly acid resin (especially Amberlite IRC–50) having been most often used. The method has proved most suitable for the more stable basic proteins of high isoelectric point and low molecular weight (Table 6.6), although in addition, Boardman and Partridge (1955) have investigated the possibilities for the chromatography of certain haemoglobins of lower isoelectric point.

TABLE 6.6. PROTEINS ISOLATED BY ION-EXCHANGE CHROMATOGRAPHY

Protein	*Reference*	*Isoelectric Point*	*Buffer pH and Composition*
Adrenotropic hormone	Dixon *et al.* (1951)	?	pH 6·8, 0·2M Na phosphate
Cytochrome-c	Boardman and Partridge (1955)	10·1	pH 7–8 Na phosphate
Chymotryp-sinogen-α	Hirs (1953)	9·1–9·5	pH 6·02 Na phosphate
Gelatin	Leach (1960)	4·95	pH 5·0 McIlvaine citric acid–phosphate
Haemoglobins	Boardman and Partridge (1955)	4·5–5·6 in citrate buffers 6·7–7·3 in phosphate	pH 5·81, 0·1M Na citrate
Lysozyme	Tallan and Stein (1953)	9·5–10	pH 7·18, 0·2M Na phosphate
Ribonuclease	Hirs, Moore and Stein (1953)	7·8	pH 6·47, 0·2M Na phosphate

The large molecules of proteins are unable to penetrate into the structure of resins even when the degree of cross-linking is low; adsorption is therefore confined to the resin surface. The capacity of the resin for proteins is thus much smaller than for small ions. The capacity for proteins, however, has been shown to increase with diminution of resin-particle size (Boardman and Partridge, 1955; Leach, 1960). The sintered structures of certain resins, such as Amberlite IRC-50, may give rise to a larger effective surface than is represented by the exterior of the individual particles.

Difficulties in the ion-exchange chromatography of proteins arise from two main causes. First of all under the conditions necessary for their separation, there may be a tendency for decomposition or denaturation of the proteins on the column. Such undesirable changes can sometimes be minimized by running the column in a cold room to slow down the rate of the denaturation reaction. The addition of an anti-oxidant, such as thiodiglycol, will help to minimize oxidation, while saturation of the eluant buffer with carbon monoxide has been used to prevent formation of methaemoglobins from CO haemoglobins.

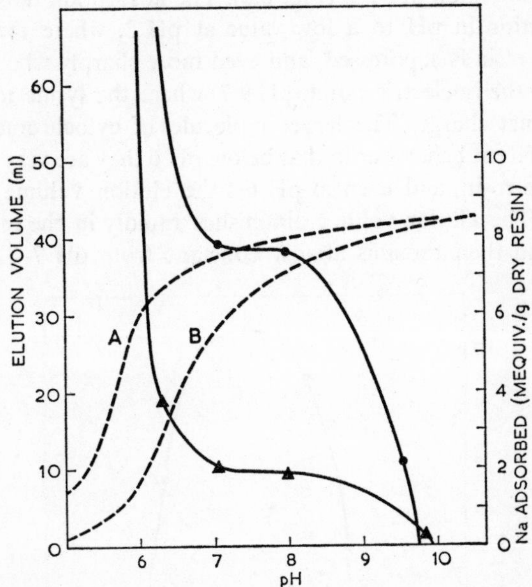

FIG. 6.5. Effect of pH on the elution of cytochrome-*c* by sodium phosphate buffers from 16 × 0·9 cm columns of Amberlite IRC–50 at 25° C. Na concentration ● 0·25 g ions/l., ▲ 0·34.
Broken lines show the amount of Na^+ taken up by the resin;
A from 1·0M NaCl. B from 0·1M NaCl.
(Boardman and Partridge, 1955. *Biochem. J.* **59,** 546).

The second type of difficulty arises from the complex nature of the interaction between proteins and ion-exchange resins. This makes prediction of suitable conditions for the chromatography of a particular protein more difficult than for smaller molecules. The ionization of the carboxylic type of resin is completely suppressed below pH 3; above this pH the carboxyl groups begin to ionize. As the degree of ionization increases so does the ability of the resin to combine with sodium ions (Fig. 6.5). The full capacity of the resin is reached in the region of pH 8–9 at which it is fully ionized. Boardman and Partridge (1955) have systematically studied the behaviour of lysine, the basic protein cytochrome-*c* and certain haemoglobins (neutral proteins), on columns of Amberlite IRC-50 over a wide pH range. The results, which throw light upon the probable behaviour of other proteins, are as follows:

The resin shows a maximum adsorption of the basic amino acid lysine, in the region pH 7–8 (Fig. 6.6). The adsorption falls sharply with reduction in pH to a low value at pH 3, where the ionization of the resin is suppressed, and even more sharply when the pH is raised to the isoelectric point (pH 9·7) where the lysine molecules have zero net charge. The larger molecules of cytochrome-c show quite a different behaviour in that below pH 6 they are very strongly held by the resin, and even at pH 6·4 the elution volume is large (Fig. 6.5). The elution volume diminishes rapidly in the region pH 6·4–7·0, and then remains almost constant from pH 7–8. Above

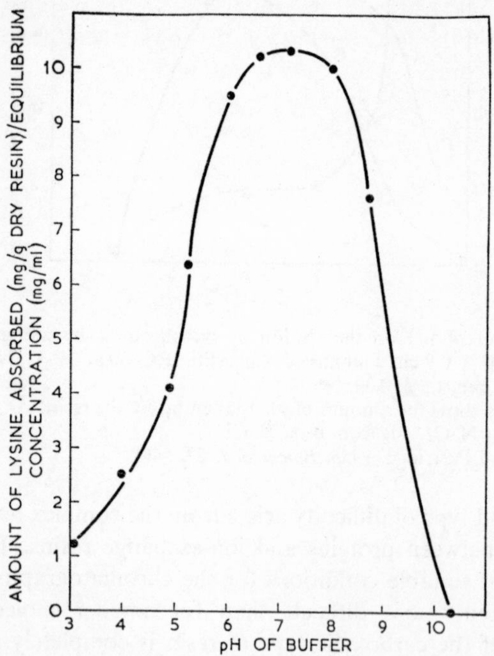

FIG. 6.6. Effect of pH on the adsorption of lysine by Amberlite IRC–50. (Boardman and Partridge, 1955. *Biochem. J.* **59,** 547).

pH 8 the affinity of the resin for cytochrome-c falls rapidly to zero at pH 10·1, the isoelectric point of the protein.

At a constant pH of 7·0, the elution volume of cytochrome-c depended critically upon the sodium-ion concentration; below 0·22 g ions/1., the protein was strongly combined with the resin but as the cation concentration was raised, the elution volume gradually decreased to a low value (Fig. 6.7). This marked dependence of the elution volume on the sodium-ion concentration of the buffer at pH 7, is in fair agreement with a theoretical ion-exchange mechanism, which postulates that each protein molecule displaces several sodium ions from the resin. The change in elution volume with pH above pH 7 can also be explained in terms of ion-exchange principles. On the other hand, the marked adsorption of cytochrome-c (and other proteins) by the carboxyl resin at low pH is in sharp contrast to the behaviour of the smaller molecules of lysine. Boardman and Partridge suggested that this effect with proteins was not due to an ion-exchange, but to the uncharged carboxyl groups of the resin. As the pH was reduced, a layer of electrostatically bound water was assumed to be removed from the resin, giving rise to a large increase in secondary short-range forces. With macromolecules such as proteins, it is known that such forces can make a large contribution to the total affinity between molecules, in this instance between protein molecule

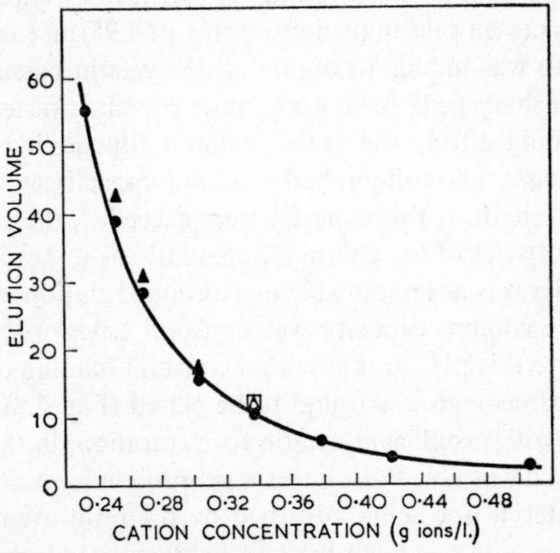

FIG. 6.7. Effect of cation concentration on the elution of cytochrome-c at pH 7·0 at 25° C, sodium and ammonium buffers.
(Boardman and Partridge, 1955. *Biochem. J.*, **59**, 546).

and resin. Of the various types of short-range forces, hydrogen bonds would seem to be more important for proteins than van der Waals' forces, owing to the polar nature of the predominant groups. Fasold *et al.* (1961), however, consider that the firm binding of proteins to carboxylic ion-exchange resins below pH 5 is not due to the formation of hydrogen bridges, as suggested by Boardman and Partridge, but to an unfolding of the protein molecules under the influence of the hydrophobic matrix of the resin.

The isoelectric points of the haemoglobins (pH 6·7–7·3 in phosphate buffer, and probably even lower in citrate as used by Boardman and Partridge) are considerably lower than that of cytochrome-c. As a result of this, there is a very rapid change in the interaction of these proteins with the resin between pH 5, where the haemoglobins are completely adsorbed on the resin, and pH 6, where the haemoglobin molecules have a net negative charge (shown on electrophoresis) and exhibit no affinity for the resin. The elution volume–pH curves for these proteins are therefore very steep and displaced to the left of the cytochrome-c curve in Fig. 6.5 as a direct consequence of the lower isoelectric points. Although there is no flat portion, as in the curve for cytochrome-c, successful chromatography is still possible by very precise control of buffer concentration and pH, in the region pH 5·8–5·9.

No conditions have been found for satisfactory chromatography of alkali-processed gelatin (isoionic point, p*I* 4·95) on carboxyl resins. Leach (1960) was unable to obtain all the gelatin passing down the column as a sharp peak having a definite R_f value. Instead there was an overloading effect, the entire column functioning as a single *theoretical plate*. The column had a definite capacity at any given pH and ionic strength. If this capacity were exceeded, the excess gelatin passed rapidly out of the column, apparently as a sharp peak, while the remainder was not removable on continued elution with the same solvent. The column capacity was constant below pH 5·5 but fell rapidly above this pH, so that with a constant loading of gelatin, an increasing percentage was found to be eluted (Fig. 6.8). By loading the column with insufficient gelatin for saturation, in the region pH 3·0–5·0, Leach was able to isolate a mucoprotein impurity from gelatin, this material not being adsorbed by the resin even at low pH, whereas the gelatin was quantitatively held on the column. Care must be taken to avoid mistaking the artificial sharp peak, resulting from overloading the column, for a separate component, since this may give rise to misconceptions concerning the homogeneity of the protein preparation, cf. Russell (1958), Leach (1960).

The most promising conditions for chromatographic separation of proteins on resins would thus appear to be on the carboxylic type, in phosphate or citrate buffers between pH 5 and 8 (Table 6.6). This is most satisfactory for proteins of high isoelectric point. The optimum pH for a convenient R_f value will be lower for proteins of

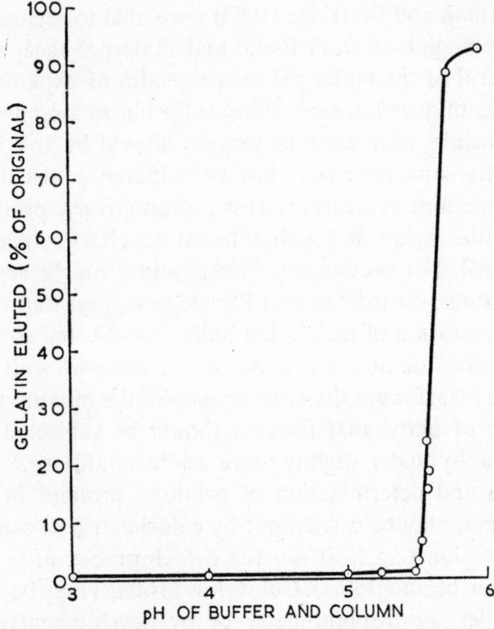

FIG. 6.8. Proportion of gelatin eluted from columns of Amberlite IRC–50 as a function of pH, with constant column loading. (Leach, 1960. *Biochem. J.* **74**, 65).

low isoelectric point, but if the latter falls below a certain limit, chromatography on this type of resin is no longer a useful method for separation.

The possibilities for chromatography of some proteins on ion-exchange resins can be extended by the addition of urea, in amounts up to 8M, to the buffer solution used for elution. This has been used to increase the solubility of insulin (Cole, 1960) and the stability of trypsin (Cole and Kinkade, 1961). Addition of urea thus permits satisfactory chromatography on ion-exchange columns and also probably reduces multiple hydrogen bonding between resin and protein, so that the ion-exchange mechanism predominates.

The isoelectric point of a protein in the buffer used for chromatography may differ substantially from its isoionic point. Properties of the protein other than the pH at which the net charge is zero, undoubtedly affect its chromatographic behaviour. The shape, size and distribution of charge all play an important part and determine what conditions, if any, are suitable for chromatographic separation. Thus Boardman and Partridge (1955) were able to separate the neutral CO haemoglobins from foetal and maternal sheep's blood by careful control of the buffer pH, while gelatin of apparently similar isoelectric point does not seem suitable for chromatographic separation. In principle, resin chromatography should be able to separate proteins of the same net charge but with different molecular patterns (e.g. lysozyme and cytochrome-c) or, alternatively, proteins of the same molecular weight but with different net charges (e.g. the sheep haemoglobins). For preliminary investigations on the separation of protein mixtures, Boardman and Partridge suggest that the pH and cation concentration of the eluting buffer be adjusted so that all the proteins in the mixture move down the column with R_f values greater than 0·5. If more than one protein of the mixture moves with an R_f value of unity, that fraction should be subjected to further chromatography under slightly more acidic conditions.

Detection and determination of coloured proteins in the eluate from a column may be carried out by colorimetric measurements in the visible region (e.g. 550 mμ for cytochrome-c, after reduction, or 412 mμ for haemoglobin). Colourless proteins may be determined by ultra-violet spectrophotometry or by development of a direct ninhydrin colour (Moore and Stein, 1948), which gives some 10 per cent of the total intensity of the constituent amino acids. The colorimetric method of Lowry *et al.* (1951) is also useful.

Nucleic-acid Components

Nucleic acids are essential constituents of all living cells and of the viruses. Among their many functions they are responsible, working in partnership with proteins, for the hereditary mechanism. Ion-exchange chromatography is playing an important part in the elucidation of the structure of these complex substances, since it provides a selective means for separating their degradation products. Although much remains to be done, some of the problems which have already been solved illustrate how elution conditions may be adjusted to suit substances with complex ionization characteristics.

Native nucleic acids have a very high molecular weight (of the order of 10^6–10^7) and are often conjugated with basic proteins of considerably lower molecular weight (protamines, histones) to form nucleoproteins. Nucleic acids are easily degraded during extraction from tissues, with considerable reduction in chain length. It is highly probable that most nucleic-acid preparations so far obtained are mixtures and do not approach the best protein preparations in purity. The nucleic acid chain consists of a large number of sub-units known as *nucleotides*; these in turn are tripartite, being composed of a phosphoric acid group, a pentose sugar (either ribose or deoxyribose) and a nitrogenous base (derived from either purine or pyrimidine). The chain is arranged so that the phosphoric acid and pentose units form alternate links, while the bases make up the short side chains.

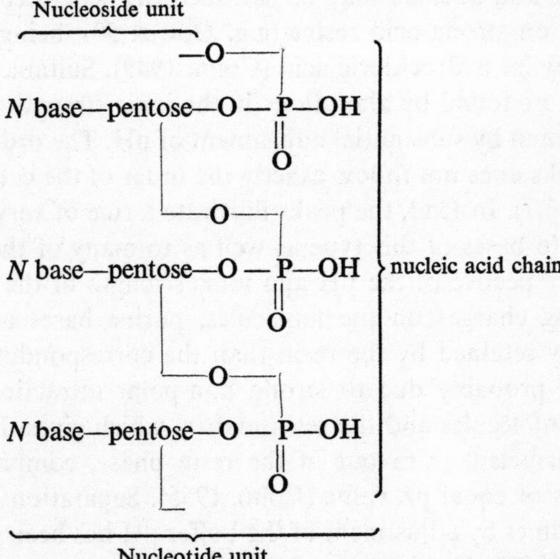

There are two main types of nucleic acids: ribonucleic acid (RNA) in which the pentose is ribose, and deoxyribonucleic acids (DNA) in which it is deoxyribose. The former predominates in cytoplasm and the latter in the cell nucleus. RNA can be completely hydrolysed to the constituent nucleotides by dilute alkali under mild conditions (0·3N potassium hydroxide, 37° C, 18 h). DNA is more stable to alkali but can be similarly hydrolysed by heating at 175° C with formic acid for 1 h in a sealed tube. Further mild hydrolysis of nucleotides results in the liberation of either the nitrogenous base and a sugar phosphate (with acid) or a *nucleoside* and phosphoric acid (with aqueous pyridine). Vigorous hydrolysis with hydrochloric acid results in complete breakdown which yields a mixture of bases, furfural (from the pentose) and phosphoric acid.

The nomenclature of the various nucleotides, nucleosides and bases found in nucleic acids is summarized in Table 6.7, together with the pK values for the ionizable groups of the bases. Any of these substances together with polynucleotides may occur as complex mixtures in nucleic-acid hydrolysates. Ion-exchange chromatography is well-suited for their separation, owing to the presence of either cationic groups on the nitrogenous bases at low pH or anionic groups derived from hydroxyl groups at relatively high pH. In addition, strongly acid phosphate groups are present in the nucleotides.

Purine and pyrimidine bases. The four bases, uracil, cytosine, guanine and adenine may be satisfactorily separated by chromatography on strong acid resins (e.g. Dowex 50), being eluted in that order by 2N hydrochloric acid (Cohn, 1949). Suitable elution conditions were found by alterations in the ionic strength of the solution rather than by substantial adjustment of pH. The order of elution of the peaks does not follow exactly the order of the catonic pK values (Table 6.7). Instead, the peaks illustrate a rule of very general application to bases of this type as well as to many of their derivatives: that irrespective of the pH and ionic strength of the eluate and the resulting charges on the molecules, purine bases are much more strongly retained by the resin than the corresponding pyrimidines. This is probably due to strong non-polar attraction between the purine molecules and the resin matrix, which gives them a distribution coefficient in favour of the resin phase, compared with pyrimidines of equal pK value (Cohn, 1955). Separation of purines and pyrimidines by adjustment of the buffer pH has been investigated by Wall (1953). For complex mixtures of substances extracted from bacteria, he used a modified form of the method designed for the chromatography of amino acids (Moore and Stein, 1951).

The nitrogenous bases can also be separated on anion-exchange resins, since where keto groups are present, these can enolize and develop ionizable hydrogens at fairly high pH (Table 6.7). The bases can be eluted in the order cytosine, uracil, thymine, guanine and

TABLE 6.7. NUCLEOTIDES, NUCLEOSIDES AND NITROGENOUS BASES FOUND IN NUCLEIC ACIDS AND p*K* VALUES FOR THE IONIZABLE GROUPS OF THE BASES

Occurrence	*Nucleotide*	*Nucleoside*	*Base*	*Structure**	p*K Values*	
					Cationic	*Anionic* (OH)
DNA	Thymidylic acid	Thymidine	Thymine	2, 6 dioxy-5-Me Py	0	9·9
Both	Adenylic acid	Adenosine	Adenine	6-amino Pu	4·1	9·8
Both	Guanylic acid	Guanosine	Guanine	2-amino-6-oxy Pu	3·2	9·5
Both	Cytidylic acid	Cytidine	Cytosine	2-oxy-6-amino Py	4·5	12·2
RNA	Uridylic acid	Uridine	Uracil	2, 6 dioxy Py	0·5	9·5
DNA	5-Methylcytidylic acid	5-Methylcytidine	5-Methylcytosine	2-oxy-5-Me-6-amino Py	4·7	12·4
	Inosinic acid†	Inosine†	Hypoxanthine†	6-oxy Pu	2·0	8·8

* Py = pyrimidine

```
      CH
    // 6 \
  N1      5CH
  |        ||
  CH2    4CH
    \\ 3 /
      N
```

Pu = purine

```
      CH
    // 6 \
  N1      5C——N
  |        ||     \\CH
  CH2    4C——NH /
    \\ 3 /
      N
```

† These result from the de-amination of adenylic acid, etc.

adenine from a Dowex 1 column in the chloride form with 0·2M ammonia, 0·025M ammonium chloride buffer at pH 10·6 (Cohn, 1949). With this anion-exchange resin, the three pyrimidines again precede the two purines. The relative positions of uracil and thymine are anomalous with respect to the p*K* values, but the extra methyl group of the latter may increase the part played by non-polar forces.

Nucleosides. The ion-exchange properties of the nucleosides do not differ greatly from those of their constituent bases, since the potentially anionic groups of the sugar residues do not ionize except under extreme alkaline conditions. Separations on cation-exchange columns are possible, but the value of the method is limited by the lability of the glycosidic bond especially of the purine nucleosides under acid conditions. The pyrimidine ribosides, cytidine and uridine, however, have been successfully separated on Zeo-Karb 215. The same resin was used for the isolation of 5-methylcytosine deoxyriboside from wheat germ (Dekkers and Elmore, 1951). Reichard and Estborn (1950) used ammonium buffers for the elution of four deoxynucleosides labelled with nitrogen-15.

Anion-exchange resins, eluted at mildly alkaline pH, provide the best general method for nucleoside separation, since under these conditions, the glycoside linkage is stable. Adenosine, cytidine and guanosine may be separated from the bases and nucleotides on Dowex 1 in the formate form, eluted with very dilute (0·01M) ammonium-formate buffers in the pH range 10–8. Addition of borate to such systems increases the adsorption of these nucleosides, which are weakly held by the resin, and makes them easier to separate (Cohn, 1955).

Nucleotides. The separation of different nucleotides may be carried out very successfully on ion-exchange columns. It has been found, in the quantitative analysis of nucleic acid hydrolysates, that separation of the nucleotides, using the hydrolysis conditions described on page 163, gives more accurate results than separation of the free purine and pyrimidine bases. The behaviour of nucleotides on ion-exchange columns differs greatly from that of the nucleosides and bases, owing to the influence of the strongly acidic phosphoryl group in the nucleotides. The p*K* values for the dissociation of the two hydrogens for these organic-phosphate esters are approximately 1 and 6 respectively compared with 2 and 7 for the inorganic phosphate ion. This difference in the strength of the phosphate groups makes possible the complete separation of inorganic phosphate from mixtures with nucleotides on basic resins such as Dowex 2 at pH 6.

The behaviour of nucleotides on anion-exchange resins below pH 7 is primarily due to the negatively charged phosphate groups. The net charge on the molecules will also be influenced by the purine and pyrimidine groups which become positively charged as the pH is reduced. This results in a decrease in the value of the net negative charge to zero (followed, for some nucleotides, by the appearance of a net positive charge) on passing through the range pH 7–0. Since the p*K* values for the basic groups vary considerably (Table 6.7), the pH dependence of net charge is different for each nucleotide. As rate of movement on an anion-exchange column increases with decrease in negative net charge, it is possible, by means of pH, to control the separation of particular groups of nucleotides. In addition to the charge effect, there is a preferential affinity of the column for purine nucleotides compared with pyrimidine ones, as already discussed for the bases. This effect is largely independent of pH and increases, approximately threefold, the elution volume for purines.

The ribonucleotides: cytidylic, adenylic, uridylic and guanylic acids, may be eluted in that order from a column of Dowex 2 resin in the chloride form, 2·5 cm high, by a 0·003N solution of hydrochloric acid (pH 2·5). The separation may be followed by direct spectrophotometry (Cohn, 1950). The positions of emergence of the various nucleotides can be explained in terms of the factors already discussed. A similar separation of the deoxynucleotides can be made with an 8-cm column of Dowex 1 resin in the chloride form, eluted successively with 0·002N and 0·003N hydrochloric acid. The order of emergence is the same with thymidylic acid taking the place of uridylic acid (Volkin *et al.*, 1951). It may be noted that in separating the components of nucleic-acid hydrolysates on anion-exchange resins, the bases and nucleosides are eluted first, followed by the nucleotides. Separation of nucleotides on cation-exchange resins is also possible, but has not been widely used.

By the use of chromatographic systems of high resolution, consisting of Dowex 1 resin eluted with dilute chloride, acetate or formate buffers, it is possible to separate each of the ribonucleotides into three distinct peaks. These have been shown to correspond to the isomeric 5′-, 2′- and 3′-phosphates which differ only in the position of attachment of the phosphate group to the ribose. The isomers are eluted in this order for all ribotides, the slight differences in properties probably being due to consistent differences in the pK values for the phosphates and amino groups, resulting from the position of the phosphate. In the RNA chain, the phosphate groups are probably attached in the 3′- and 5′- positions, the 2′- nucleotide arising by isomerization during hydrolysis. In DNA the 2′- position is not available so the linkage must be 3′, 5′. Comparison of the relative occurrence of the three types of isomeric nucleotide in enzymic and alkaline digests has been used to throw light on the structure of the nucleic acids.

Polyphosphates. As the number of phosphate groups in polyphosphate compounds increases, so does the adsorption on anion-exchange resins, with a corresponding increase in elution volume. It is possible to elute adenosine monophosphate (AMP), inorganic phosphate, ADP, ATP and inorganic hexametaphosphate in that order from a Dowex 1 column with 0·01N hydrochloric acid and stepwise increases in chloride concentration.

Polynucleotides. Mixtures of polynucleotides, derived by the action of enzymes or by partial acid hydrolysis of the nucleic acids, may be resolved by chromatography on anion-exchange resins. These may be eluted with dilute hydrochloric acid, with increasing acid and chloride-ion concentrations. The larger size of the molecules needs to be taken into account when selecting the cross-linkage of the resin. Whereas molecules up to the size of at least tetranucleotides can be well separated on anion-exchange resins with a 2 per cent cross-linked polystyrene matrix, using a chloride system, excessive broadening of the peaks takes place on 10 per cent cross-linked resin (Cohn, 1955). Ion-exchange chromatography would seem to be a powerful tool for investigating the structure of nucleic acids by resolving complex mixtures of polynucleotides.

REFERENCES

Bender, A. E., Palgrave, J. A. and Doell, B. H. (1959). *Analyst* **84,** 526.
Boardman, N. K. and Partridge, S. M. (1955). *Biochem. J.* **59,** 543.
Brenner, M. and Burckhardt, C. H. (1951). *Helv. Chim. Acta* **34,** 1070.
Brown, A. H. (1946). *Arch. Biochem.* **11,** 269.
Cohn, W. E. (1949). *Science* **109,** 377.
Cohn, W. E. (1950). *J. Amer. chem. Soc.* **72,** 1471.
Cohn, W. E. (1955). *Nucleic Acids* I, 211, ed. Chargaff and Davidson, Academic Press, New York.

Cole, R. D. (1960). *J. biol. Chem.* **235,** 2294.
Cole, R. D. and Kinkade, J. M. (1961). *J. biol. Chem.* **236,** 2443.
Crumpton, M. J. (1959). *Biochem. J.* **72,** 479.
Dekkers, C. A. and Elmore, D. T. (1951). *J. Chem. Soc.* 2864.
Dixon, H. B. F., Moore, S., Stack-Dunne, M. P. and Young, F. G. (1951). *Nature, Lond.* **168,** 1044.
Dowmont, Y. P. and Fruton, J. S. (1952). *J. biol. Chem.* **197,** 271.
Dreywood, R. (1946). *Ind. Eng. Chem. Anal. Edn.* **18,** 499.
Eastoe, J. E. (1954). *Nature, Lond.* **173,** 540.
Eastoe, J. E. (1961). *Biochem. J.* **79,** 652.
Fasold, H., Gundlach, G. and Turba, F. (1961). *Chromatography,* 378, ed. by E. Heftmann, Reinhold Publ. Corp., New York.
Gardell, S. (1953). *Acta chem. Scand.* **7,** 207.
Hamilton, P. B. (1958). *Analyt. Chem.* **30,** 914.
Hirs, C. H. W. (1953). *J. biol. Chem.* **205,** 93.
Hirs, C. H. W., Moore, S. and Stein, W. H. (1953). *J. biol. Chem.* **200,** 493.
Hirs, C. H. W., Moore, S. and Stein, W. H. (1956). *J. biol. Chem.* **219,** 623.
Hirs, C. H. W., Stein, W. H. and Moore, S. (1956). *J. biol. Chem.* **221,** 151.
Ketelle, B. H. and Boyd, G. E. (1947). *J. Amer. chem. Soc.* **69,** 2800.
Ketelle, B. H. and Boyd, G. E. (1951). *J. Amer. chem. Soc.* **73,** 1862.
Khym, J. X. and Cohn, W. E. (1953). *J. Amer. chem. Soc.* **75,** 1153.
Khym, J. X. and Zill, L. P. (1951). *J. Amer. chem. Soc.* **73,** 2399; **74,** 2090; **75,** 1339.
Leach, A. A. (1960). *Biochem. J.* **74,** 61.
Lowry, O. H., Rosebrough, N. J., Farr, A. L. and Randall, R. J. (1951). *J. biol. Chem.* **193,** 265.
Moore, S., Spackman, D. H. and Stein, W. H. (1958). *Analyt. Chem.* **30,** 1185.
Moore, S. and Stein, W. H. (1948). *J. biol. Chem.* **176,** 367.
Moore, S. and Stein, W. H. (1951). *J. biol. Chem.* **192,** 663.
Moore, S. and Stein, W. H. (1954). *J. biol. Chem.* **211,** 893.
Partridge, S. M. (1951). *J. sci. Instrum.* **28,** 28.
Partridge, S. M. and Brimley, R. C. (1951). *Biochem. J.* **49,** 153.
Partridge, S. M. and Davis, H. F. (1955). *Biochem. J.* **61,** 21.
Partridge, S. M. and Westall, R. G. (1949). *Biochem. J.* **44,** 418.
Piez, K. A. and Morris, L. (1960). *Analyt. Biochem.* **1,** 187.
Piez, K. A. and Saroff, H. A. (1961). *Chromatography,* 347, ed. by E. Heftmann, Reinhold Publ. Corp., New York.
Reichard, P. and Estborn, B. (1950). *Acta chem. Scand.* **4,** 1047.
Rudloff, V. and Braunitzer, G. (1961). *Zeit. physiol. Chem.* **323,** 129.
Russell, G. (1958). *Nature, Lond.* **181,** 102.
Schroeder, W. A., Honnen, L. and Green, F. C. (1953). *Proc. Nat. Acad. Sci. U.S.* **39,** 23.
Spackman, D. H., Stein, W. H. and Moore, S. (1958). *Analyt. Chem.* **30,** 1190.
Spedding, F. H. (1949). *Discuss. Faraday Soc.* **7,** 214.

Stein, W. H. and Moore, S. (1950). *Cold Spring Harb. Symp. quant. Biol.* **14**, 179.
Tallan, H. H. and Stein, W. H. (1953). *J. biol. Chem.* **200**, 507.
Volkin, E., Khym, J. X. and Cohn, W. E. (1951). *J. Amer. chem. Soc.* **73**, 1533.
Wall, J. S. (1953). *Analyt. Chem.* **25**, 950.

CHAPTER 7
SPECIALIZED CHROMATOGRAPHIC SYSTEMS

Progress in chromatography depends upon the discovery or deliberate development of media for the stationary phase, with structures and properties peculiarly suited to the separation of particular types of substance. Many of the possibilities of the media readily available have already been explored, and increasing attention is being directed towards the production of new types. In addition, new and more convenient ways of exploiting the properties of the well-established adsorbents are being found. The use, in columns, of ion-exchange resins, available for the last fifteen years, has already been described; an alternative employment of these resins incorporated in sheets of paper will now be given. Among other recently introduced media, Sephadex and the substituted dextrans, which appear to be very promising, particularly in the biochemical field, are discussed in this chapter.

By the use of chromatograms of optimum physical form, greatly increased convenience, speed and sensitivity can be attained. Thus *thin-layer* methods permit the special advantages, associated with paper chromatography, to be obtained with a variety of adsorbents previously used only in columns.

Modified Cellulose and Dextran Ion-exchangers

Ion-exchange resins have a backbone or matrix, to which the ionizable groups are attached, which is strongly hydrophobic, since it usually consists of a cross-linked aromatic hydrocarbon network. The forces between any ion-exchange medium and substances adsorbed on it are basically of two kinds—ionic and non-ionic. The ionic forces of electrostatic attraction or repulsion between charged groups on the ion-exchange medium and the substances undergoing separation come readily to mind, but non-ionic forces between the backbone of the medium and non-ionized parts of the molecules also play a decisive part in determining the relative affinities of different substances for the medium, and hence the degree of separation which can be achieved. The hydrophobic nature of resin matrices restricts the non-ionic forces to the van der Waals' type of interaction with hydrophobic (lipophilic) parts of the adsorbed molecules, there being little opportunity for hydrogen bond formation with the more hydrophilic groups of the molecules.

This imposes two limitations on the use of such resins in chromatography. First, there will be little or no non-ionic interaction between predominantly hydrophilic substances and the resin, which may limit the possibilities of separation for substances of this type. Second, delicate substances of a biological origin, which normally have a predominantly hydrophilic environment, may be denatured by the disorientation produced by van der Waals' bonding between lipophilic regions in any part of the molecule and the resin matrix.

Such limitations have been overcome recently by the introduction of ion-exchange media with a hydrophilic type of matrix. These are prepared by reactions which introduce ionizable groups into insoluble carbohydrate polymers such as cellulose and dextran. The matrix thus obtained consists almost entirely of anhydroglucose units joined in ether linkage through the 1,4 carbon atoms in the modified celluloses and the 1,6 atoms in the modified dextrans (modified Sephadex, see page 178).

Various groupings have been successfully introduced into cellulose which give rise to strongly and weakly acidic cation-exchangers and strongly and weakly basic anion-exchangers (Table 7.1). Some of these are available commercially, the cation-exchange celluloses being supplied in different exchange capacities. Cellulose phosphate contains one very weak and one more strongly acidic group, which enables it to function down to pH 2 and to adsorb some metallic cations from acidic solutions (Head *et al.*, 1958). Carboxymethyl cellulose has a p*K* value in the region 3·8–4·3 in water and 3·5–3·7 in 0·5M sodium chloride solution and is most often used at pH 5 and above. It has a low exchange capacity but has been found particularly useful in the protein field.

Aminoethyl cellulose is a weakly basic anion-exchanger which exhibits its full capacity only below pH 5. DEAE cellulose is rather more strongly basic, since it has tertiary amine groupings. It has probably been the most widely used of the anion-exchange celluloses, particularly for the separation of proteins. ECTEOLA cellulose has a

Table 7.1. Modified Cellulose Ion-exchangers

Exchanger	*Groups*	*Abbreviation*	*Exchange Capacity**	*Reference*
Cation-exchangers				
Strongly acidic				
Cellulose phosphate	$—O—P(=O)(O^-)_2$	P	1·0†, 4·2†, 7·4†	Peterson and Sober (1956)
Sulphomethyl cellulose	$—O—CH_2—S(=O)_2—O^-$	SM		Porath (1957)
Sulphoethyl cellulose	$—O—CH_2.CH_2—S(=O)_2—O^-$	SE		Porath (1957)
Weakly acidic				
Carboxymethyl cellulose	$—O—CH_2—C(=O)—O^-$	CM	0·3, 0·7	Peterson and Sober (1956)
Anion-exchangers				
Strongly basic				
Triethylaminoethyl cellulose	$—O—CH_2.CH_2—N^+(Et)_2—Et$	TEAE		Porath (1957)
Weakly basic				
Diethylaminoethyl cellulose	$—O—CH_2.CH_2—NH^+(Et)_2$	DEAE	1·0	Peterson and Sober (1956)
Aminoethyl cellulose	$—O—CH_2.CH_2—NH_3{}^+$	AE	1·0	Peterson and Sober (1956)
Ecteola cellulose (epichlorhydrin + triethanolamine)	$—N^+ (CH_2.CH_2.OH)_3$	ECTEOLA	0·5	Peterson and Sober (1956)

* Expressed in m-equiv/g. Where values are given for exchange capacities, the modified cellulose is available in this country.

† Total exchange capacities, the capacities of the strongly acidic groups are one half of these values.

more complex structure since it is partially cross-linked by the epichlorhydrin used in its preparation. It has been found particularly useful for the chromatographic separation of nucleic acids (Bendich *et al.*, 1955).

The hydrophilic nature of the cellulose matrix gives it a high water-binding capacity, resulting in considerable swelling in aqueous solutions. The swollen structure is presumably more readily permeable to large molecules such as proteins than the hydrophobic cross-linked structure of resins since, despite their low degree of substitution with exchangeable groups (0·5–1 m-equiv/g), modified celluloses have a large effective capacity for macromolecules of a polyelectrolyte type. Thus, the molecules of even sensitive proteins are gently adsorbed on the matrix and can be eluted from the ion-exchange cellulose without decomposition, under less drastic conditions than from a resin.

Modified celluloses should be allowed to swell and should be equilibrated with the initial eluting solution before the column is poured for chromatography. A high degree of substitution with ionizable groups should be avoided as this results in gel-like columns which have very poor flow rates. The pH values of buffers chosen for elution should be such that the groups on the cellulose are completely or almost completely ionized, the most useful pH range being just within to somewhat beyond the titration range of the groupings. The buffering ion should not react with the column material and should be chosen to have a charge of the same sign as the ionized groups on the cellulose (e.g. cationic buffers for anion-exchange cellulose and anionic buffers for cation-exchange cellulose). The ether derivatives of cellulose, e.g. CM, SM, SE, TEAE, DEAE, and AE cellulose (for abbreviations see Table 7.1), are reasonably stable and may be used under a wide range of conditions. The ester derivatives, cellulose phosphate and citrate, are liable to become hydrolysed at low or high pH.

As mentioned previously, ion-exchange celluloses are particularly useful for the chromatography of labile substances, especially proteins (Table 7.2), nucleotides, nucleic acids and antibiotics. Sober and Peterson (1960) have given a clear picture of the probable mechanism of chromatography on modified celluloses and the principles underlying control of elution. With large molecules such as proteins, both the substance to be separated and the ion-exchange cellulose are polyelectrolytes, and are therefore capable of interaction at a number of points. The adsorbed protein is therefore more tightly bound than a substance with a single charged group under the same conditions. Nevertheless, it is possible to elute the protein by changing the pH, so reducing the number of charges on the protein (or less selectively, on the modified cellulose), or alternatively, by increasing the salt or buffer-ion concentration of the eluant so as to compete for the charges on the ion-exchange cellulose. In Fig. 7.1 is shown the separa-

TABLE 7.2. CONDITIONS USED FOR SEPARATION OF PROTEINS ON MODIFIED CELLULOSE

Modified Cellulose	*Protein*	*Conditions*
CM	Egg white proteins	0·1M NH_4 acetate buffer, stepwise pH changes 4·4, 4·6, 4·8, 5·0, 5·5, 6·0, 6·7, 8·5, 9·5, 10·0
CM	Haemoglobins	0·01M phosphate buffer, gradient elution, pH 6·0 to 8·0
CM	Pancreatic enzymes	Phosphate buffer, gradient elution, 0·01M, pH 6·0 to 0·1M, pH 6·5
CM	Ribonuclease	pH 8·0 buffer, NaCl gradient 0–0·1M
DEAE	Albumin	Sodium phosphate buffer, pH 7·1, concentration gradient, 0·005–0·30M
DEAE	Enzymes from E. coli	Potassium phosphate buffer 0·01M, pH 7·0, NaCl gradient, 0–0·5M
DEAE	Serum proteins	'Tris'-phosphate buffer, pH 8·6, concave gradient, 0·005–0·35M
DEAE	Spleen nuclease	Sodium phosphate buffer, concentration and pH gradient, 0·005M, pH 7 to 0·2M, pH 5·5

tion of the first twenty members of the homologous series of lysine polypeptides by means of a gradient of sodium chloride.

For any given surface charge-density, rather stronger eluting conditions are usually necessary for large molecules than for small ones, owing to the greater number of bonds which can be formed with the ion-exchanger. Thus, Staehelin *et al.* (1959) separated successive peaks of polyadenylic acid containing from two to six adenylic acid units from DEAE cellulose, eluted with ammonium bicarbonate buffer of pH 8·6 and increasing concentration.

Factors affecting the chromatographic behaviour of a protein include the net surface charge-density, the arrangement of the charge in space, molecular size and non-ionic forces. Only the effect of net charge determines the migration rate for electrophoresis in free solution. For this reason chromatography and electrophoresis have different potentialities for bringing about separation. As an example, two proteins with different net charge-densities, which could be separated by electrophoresis, would not be separable by chromatography if there were an exactly compensating effect from the other factors. On the other hand, it is sometimes possible to separate, chromatographically, a pair of proteins with equal net charges but differing, for example, in molecular size. The lack of correspondence between these two methods of separation has been observed frequently in practice, and is indeed very useful, since one method can

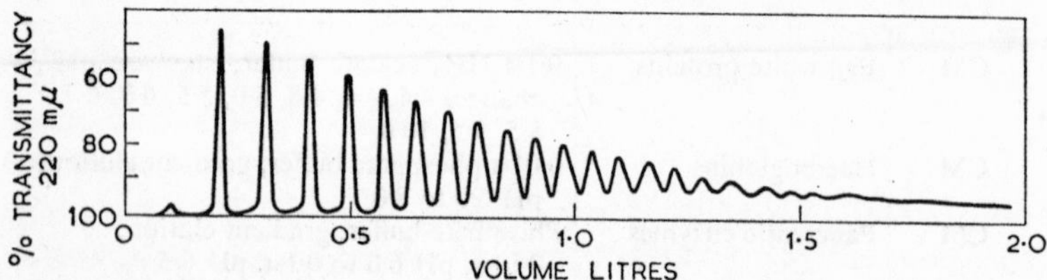

FIG. 7.1. Chromatogram developed on a 40 × 0·9 cm column of 4 g carboxymethylcellulose (0·7 m-equiv./g capacity, Na^+ form) with an exponential gradient of NaCl. The 1 litre constant volume mixing flask, initially filled with water, was replenished with 0·82M NaCl (after 2 litres of flow, with 1·73M NaCl) at 2·0 ml/min. A partial acid hydrolysate of 30 mg high molecular weight polylysine was applied to the column. (Stewart and Stahmann (1962). *J. Chromatog.* **9**, 233).

be used to supplement the other when either technique alone fails to achieve complete resolution of a mixture.

Sober and Peterson (1960) have pointed out that when a mixture of proteins is applied to a column of modified cellulose, which is then eluted with a buffer solution, some of the proteins (a) will remain at the top of the column, tightly bound by many electrostatic bonds, so long as the initial elution conditions are continued. Another group of proteins (c) which form very few bonds with the ion-exchanger will move down the column almost as fast as the solvent. With any given elution conditions, the possibility arises that a third category of proteins (b) will have an intermediate number of charged groups, that is just sufficient for there to be a reasonable chance of all the electrostatic bonds being broken simultaneously, so that the molecules move with the solvent for a short distance before re-forming electrostatic bonds at another site on the ion-exchange cellulose.

Proteins in this group will slowly pass down the column by a truly chromatographic mechanism, and if they move at different rates, they will be separated from one another, provided that the column is sufficiently long.

If the composition of the eluting solution is now changed, so as to reduce the number of electrostatic bonds between the proteins and ion-exchange cellulose, some of the original stationary proteins will move down the column. The number of charges on the protein molecules may be very sensitive to changes in solvent composition, and if too large a change is made, some of the proteins will pass from (a) directly to state (c) so that there will be no chance of separating them by means of the more sensitive chromatographic process (b). It is better instead, to alter the composition of the eluting solvent very gradually, preferably by infinitesimal steps, as in gradient elution (see also page 29). Each protein then begins to move from the top of the column at the exact point where the solvent composition reduces protein-cellulose interaction just sufficiently to allow migration. As the band of protein moves down the column, it will be overtaken by solvent of increasing eluting power; this causes both an acceleration of the band and a sharpening of its edges. If the column is sufficiently long, the protein band will ultimately move at the same speed as the solvent, at which stage no benefit as regards increased resolution will be gained by increasing the length of the column. For this reason, it is essential to match the steepness of the gradient used, to the particular length of column necessary to achieve a desired degree of resolution.

Gradient elution has two main advantages over stepwise changes of solvent for the chromatography of substances such as proteins. First, gradient elution avoids the rapid creation of conditions under which complete desorption takes place, favouring instead those conditions suitable for true chromatography. Second, where a mixture of unknown proteins is to be investigated chromatographically, artefacts are readily produced during stepwise elution, due to the newly-changed solvent catching up with the tail of a slow-moving peak, after the main portion of the peak has left the column, and thereby sharpening it into a second peak of the same substance. A similar effect may occur if the column is initially overloaded, since the excess protein is rapidly eluted. Gradient elution is therefore much more useful and can often reveal a clear overall picture of the protein components in a complex mixture from a biological source.

Provided that a suitably-shaped gradient is used, each peak will represent a separate constituent. The optimum design of gradient for any particular mixture can only be determined by 'trial and error' experiments. It is sometimes useful to change both the pH and the salt concentration of the eluting solution, simultaneously, since the overall range of each type of change will be minimized, and extreme conditions likely to decompose very unstable compounds will therefore be avoided.

The very gentle interaction between proteins and the hydrophilic ion-exchange cellulose sometimes makes it possible for loosely associated complexes to survive the chromatographic process without breakdown. This is intrinsically an advantage of cellulose media, provided that steps are ultimately taken to recognize the individual components of such a complex, which has appeared as a single peak. For example, certain albumins may form complexes with lipids, derived from stopcock grease or dialysis tubing, in the course of experimental procedures (Sober and Peterson, 1958). These are stable during chromatography on modified cellulose and so give rise to puzzling artefacts.

The ion-exchange derivatives of the dextran polymer Sephadex have not yet been available for a sufficient length of time for their advantages, if any, over the cellulose derivatives with the same functional groups to have become clear. The potentiality of these materials for separation of small as well as large molecules, has, however, been shown by the successful chromatography of amino acids and small peptides on DEAE Sephadex A25. This was achieved by application of a gradient of pH by means of 0·1M and then M acetic acid to a chromatogram which had been equilibrated with 0·1M collidine acetate buffer at pH 8·55. As the pH fell, the amino acids emerged in the order to be expected from the p*K* values of their amino groups. The aromatic amino acids were slightly adsorbed but to a lesser degree than they would have been on Dowex 1. Since the neutral small peptides such as leucylglycylglycine were eluted as sharp peaks when the pH of the eluate fell below 8, they were easily separated from the dicarboxylic amino acids which did not emerge until pH 7·0.

Two grades of DEAE Sephadex are available which differ only in their degree of cross-linkage. The more highly cross-linked A25 grade, used for the above separations, is unsuitable for the chromatography of molecules larger than 10,000 mol. wt. because this is the limiting size for entry into the gel particles. The less cross-linked A50 grade is more porous and as a result, can bind six times as much pepsin as that taken up by the A25 grade. The total exchange capacity of DEAE Sephadex is 3 m-equiv./g. In practice a column made from 1 g of DEAE Sephadex A50 can be used for the chromatography of 3 ml of serum.

Sephadex is also available, substituted with carboxymethyl groups, to give the weak cation-exchanger CM Sephadex and with sulphoethyl groups to give the strong cation-exchanger SE Sephadex. Once again only in the C50 types are all the groups available for exchange of molecules larger than 10,000 mol. wt. The C25 types, on the other hand, are advantageous for small molecules due to their higher capacity per unit volume.

The following details for pretreatment of CM and SE Sephadex are given by the manufacturers:

(1) Swell in water for one hour and remove some of the finest particles by decantation.
(2) Wash on a filter with 0·5N sodium hydroxide followed by a large amount of water.
(3) Wash briefly with 0·5N hydrochloric acid followed by water.
(4) Equilibrate with the appropriate buffer.

DEAE Sephadex should be prepared in the same way except that the 0·5N hydrochloric acid treatment should precede that with 0·5N sodium hydroxide.

Sephadex

A significant advance in chromatography has been made possible by the introduction of the cross-linked dextran polymer known as Sephadex (Porath and Flodin, 1959). Gels with varying properties are obtained by polymerization of dextran with different amounts of epichlorhydrin; the degree of cross-linkage then obtained determines those properties of the gel which are most important for chromatography. Gels with high cross-linkage, showing low water regains, are only useful for the separation, from one another, of molecules small enough to diffuse into the gel. On the other hand, gels with a low degree of cross-linkage and high water regain, can be used for the fractionation of relatively large molecules because these can enter such gels. In Table 7.3 are shown some of the properties of the five types of Sephadex so far available.

Sephadex gels can be used for two main types of operation; these may be called 'crude' and 'refined' separations. Crude separations are those where one of the substances can enter the pores of the gel particles while another cannot. If such a mixture of substances is allowed to pass down a chromatogram packed with particles of a suitable grade of Sephadex, the non-entering substance will move at the rate of the solvent front, whereas those which can enter the particles of gel will move with a rate determined by the partition coefficient between the stationary aqueous phase in the particles and

TABLE 7.3. SOME PROPERTIES OF SEPHADEX GELS

Type	*Water Regain* g/g	*Size of Molecules Completely Excluded* mol. wt.	*Suitable Loading for Fractionation* g/g dry gel	*Swelling Factor* ml/g
G 25	2·5	3,500–4,500	—	5
G 50	5·0	8,000–10,000	0·18	10
G 75	7·5	40,000–50,000	—	14
G 100	10·0	100,000	—	20
G 200	20·2	200,000	0·08	40

the moving phase. An example of such a mixture is that of an inorganic salt and a protein. By means of a column of Sephadex G 25 these separations are easily achieved. The process is similar to dialysis but has the advantage that it can be carried out much more rapidly.

For refined separations to be possible, all the substances to be separated must enter the pores of the gel particles. When substances of different molecular sizes are present, they will be found to enter the individual gel particles in different degrees. That is to say, the proportion of water in the gel particle that is available for the dissolution of a larger molecule is less than the proportion available for the dissolution of a smaller one. The reason for this is believed to be the existence of so-called 'forbidden' regions at the sites of cross-linkage. The abilities of molecules of different sizes to diffuse into the gel particles are reflected in differences of partition coefficient between the stationary and moving phases and thus in different R_f values. Different available volumes in the gel particles have been found for tritiated water and for the alkali metal chlorides, some relationship has been found between the hydrated ionic radius and the available water space. As an example, only 70 per cent of the imbibed water is accessible to sucrose.

Since Sephadex gels consist only of dextran polymerized with epichlorhydrin, they are essentially chains of glucose residues joined by 1,6-glucosidic bonds, cross-linked by glyceryl bridges in ether linkage derived from the epichlorhydrin (Flodin, 1962). The only ionizable groups present are hydroxyls which are uncharged at neutral pH values. When neutral polysaccharides and similar non-polar molecules are present, the gel particles act as already described. These and many other separations which are based on the varying ability of molecules to diffuse into the gel are due to so-called molecular sieve effects.

Except when the ionized groups on the gel are concerned, any convenient electrolyte can be used and interactions, such as those between protein molecules due to electrostatic forces, can be minimized by the use of media of high ionic strength. In fact when proteins and peptides are chromatographed on Sephadex, the separations are usually due to molecular sieve effects. When low ionic-strength buffers are used, however, adsorption and ion-exclusion effects may sometimes become important. Even in 0·2M acetic acid, it has been found that not all peptides obtained by tryptic digestion of the α chain of human haemoglobin separate on the basis of size. Another example of behaviour due to charge effects is that, when dinitrophenylaspartic acid is chromatographed with distilled water, it is almost completely excluded from the gel. If, on the other hand, a solution of sodium chloride is used for elution, this substance is so greatly retarded that not only must it have entered the gel particles but it must also have been adsorbed on the matrix. Glutamic acid, glycine, phenylalanine, tyrosine and tryptophan have been separated as symmetrical peaks on Sephadex G 25 (200–400 mesh) clearly indicating that all these amino acids have linear adsorption isotherms. In addition, nucleic-acid components have been resolved due to their differing degrees of adsorption.

Sufficient experience of the chromatographic behaviour of many different classes of substances on Sephadex G 25, G 50, and G 75 has already accumulated for a fairly adequate understanding of the nature of the various processes. Unfortunately, it is, as yet, too early for a similar claim to be made in respect of the lightly cross-linked grades G 100 and G 200. The pores of these gels are large enough for proteins of molecular weight up to approximately 100,000 and 200,000 to be able to enter respectively the pores of the G 100 and G 200 grades. When plasma is chromatographed on the G 100 grade two peaks are formed, the slower of which consists mainly of albumin. Using the G 200 grade, the plasma divides into three peaks. Re-running material from both the experiments with Sephadex G 200 itself and by paper electrophoresis has shown all of these peaks to be complex, division into more than one peak during rechromatography on Sephadex G 200 depending primarily on the presence of sodium chloride.

Properties of the Gels and Construction of Columns. The water regain of the various types of Sephadex is shown in Table 7.3. Solubility tests at room temperature on the G 25, G 50 and G 75 grades have shown 0·1–1·0 per cent of the gel to be in solution at the end of 24 h; subsequently, release of soluble carbohydrate falls to between 0·002 and 0·003 per cent/24 h. At room temperatures these gels have been found to be stable to 0·02N hydrochloric acid for long periods. The G 25, G 50 and G 75 grades are supplied in three ranges of particle size. When the narrower size ranges are required, fractionation by dry sieving can be used. Particles passing sieves finer than 200 (U.S. Standard Screen Series) are more conveniently handled by decantation. The particles which make up these three grades are irregularly shaped as they are formed by disintegration of a solid material prepared by a polymerization process. As in other forms of chromatography, columns consisting of fine particles will always give sharper bands; however, the advantage of using the finer grades of Sephadex has to be balanced against the disadvantage of inconveniently slow separations. Slow rates of flow can be increased by the use of greater pressures across the column. When this is achieved by means of a pumping system, care must be taken to avoid dangerous rises in pressure. For a 50-cm column of Sephadex G 25 of the medium grade, a flow rate of 0·8 ml cm^{-2} min^{-1} should be given by a driving pressure of 3 m of water.

Particle aggregation during the process of swelling and decantation will be avoided if a dilute solution of sodium chloride or of buffer salt is present. Care should be taken to ensure that swelling is complete before any attempt is made to pack the chromatogram. For grades G 25 and G 50, a few hours will suffice for this process, whereas for the lower cross-linked grades 24 h will be found necessary. Since Grades G 100 and G 200 are polymerized as beads, much less finely divided material is present and preliminary decantation is not usually required. Regularly packed columns are, of course, very important. For tubes up to 4 cm in diameter this may be ensured as follows. First, a piece of glass wool is pressed into the bottom of the column, shaped to give a narrow exit; the glass wool is then covered with a layer of fine glass beads. Next an extension tube, at least as long as the column itself, is attached to the top. The column is then filled approximately one-third full with buffer solution, and a suspension of the Sephadex, sufficient to fill the column and the extension tube, is then added. Soon after the Sephadex has started to settle, the exit at the bottom of the tube is opened and a slow stream of buffer is allowed to flow out. As the extension tube empties, further suspension is added until the packed zone is of sufficient height. Preliminary washing of the column, with the first buffer to be used in the separation, is continued until no further contraction can be observed.

Application of the Sample. This can be done by the normal technique of running the solution on to the top surface of the packed Sephadex with no free buffer solution present. In these circumstances it is often desirable to protect the surface of the exchanger by placing on it a circle of filter paper. Alternatively, the solution to be analysed can be introduced a few millimetres above the surface of the Sephadex, without preliminary removal of the eluting buffer. To make this possible the tip of a very narrow plastic tube, connected to a motor-driven syringe, is lowered to the appropriate level, the sample is then forced in at a rate not above 3 ml/min. This method is only applicable if the sample solution is so much denser than the solution with which it is to be eluted, that little mixing can take place. Fortunately, if this is not so, sodium chloride or sucrose can be dissolved in the sample solution to increase the density. Because of the special properties of Sephadex these additional materials are usually eluted at a slower rate than the substances undergoing analysis.

Ion-exchange Papers

Specially prepared papers with ion-exchange properties have recently become available which make it possible to combine the particular advantages of ion-exchange separations with the convenience of paper chromatography. The techniques with such ion-exchange papers are very similar to those used in filter-paper chromatography as regards the method of supporting the paper in a closed tank, development and spraying. As well as organic solvent mixtures, aqueous buffer solutions of controlled pH and ionic strength, and mixtures of organic solvents with buffer solutions are commonly used for developing the chromatograms. Sometimes it is advantageous to hang the papers in the tank initially and allow the solvent to travel down them in order to establish equilibrium between solvent and paper and to remove impurities. The paper may then be carefully blotted and the spots containing substances to be separated applied to the slightly damp paper. This 'wet start' technique has the advantage that the paper need not be dried before applying the spots.

Two types of ion-exchange papers are available, one of which consists of modified cellulose in which the ionizable groups are directly attached to the cellulose of the paper, giving it properties similar to the modified celluloses used in column chromatography. The wet strength of certain modified cellulose papers may be rather low. The second type of paper has ordinary cellulose fibres loaded with one of the various types of ion-exchange resin. Cation- and anion-exchange papers of strongly and weakly acidic or basic types are available in both modified cellulose and resin-loaded forms (Table 7.4).

A particular attraction of ion-exchange papers is the possibility of using a two-dimensional technique in which conditions are arranged so as to favour separation by the ion-exchange mechanism in one direction and by the partition mechanism, characteristic of ordinary paper chromatography, in the other direction. The latter condition can be achieved by the use of an organic-solvent mixture, adjusted to a pH such that the ionization of groups on the paper is suppressed. Alternatively the pH may be adjusted so that all the molecules being separated carry charges of the same sign as the ionized groups on the paper. By appropriate choice of pH, amphoteric substances such as the amino acids can be made to carry the same charge as either basic or acidic substituted papers. In this way, use can be made of different properties of the migrating substances in the two directions, so as to obtain good separations without employing the elaborate multi-component solvent mixtures sometimes used in chromatography on unsubstituted papers. These mixtures, though capable of giving good separation, do not easily yield reproducible results, owing to undue sensitivity to such factors as temperature. A useful criterion of the success of the two-dimensional separations is that the spots should be distributed as widely as possible over the whole area of the paper and not concentrated near the diagonal or confined to one half of the paper.

Good separations of a number of metal ions (Cu, Mn, Co, Cd, Fe, Bi, Zn and Hg) have been obtained by Knight (1959a) by descending chromatography on 14-in. squares of paper consisting of phosphorylated or carboxylated cellulose. Butanol, saturated with 2N hydrochloric acid, was used as organic phase in the first direction,

TABLE 7.4. ION-EXCHANGE PAPERS

Class	*Name of Paper*	*Ionizable Group*	*Exchange Capacity* (m-equiv./g)
Whatman modified cellulose paper			
Fairly strong acid	Cellulose phosphate	Phosphate	2·1
Weak acid	Carboxymethyl cellulose	Carboxyl	0·5
Weak base	Aminoethyl cellulose	Primary amine	0·6
Weak base	Diethyl aminoethyl cellulose	Secondary amine	0·4
Weak base	ECTEOLA cellulose	—	0·3
Amberlite ion-exchange resin paper			
Strong acid	SA-2 (with IR-120 resin, Na^+ form)	Sulphonic acid	1·9 (0·03)*
Weak acid	WA-2 (with IRC-50 resin, H^+ form)	Carboxylic acid	4·6 (0·06)*
Strong base	SB-2 (with IRA-400 resin, Cl^- form)	Quaternary ammonium	1·5 (0·02)*
Weak base	WB-2 (with IR-4B resin, OH^- form)	Primary and secondary amine	3·0 (0·04)*

* Values in brackets are in m-equiv./cm^2.

and at the low pH value thus obtained, the ionization of the acidic groups on the cellulose was suppressed so that the migration of the ions occurred in a manner similar to that on unmodified cellulose. When the chromatogram was dried in the presence of ammonia, the acid was neutralized and the phosphate converted to its ionized form. Development in the second direction with N magnesium chloride solution then permitted exchange to occur between the various metals and magnesium. Finally the position of the spots was revealed by spraying with a pentacyanoamminoferrate–rubeanic acid complex to produce characteristic colours. Satisfactory results were also obtained very rapidly on 8-in. squares of phosphorylated paper developed by the ascending method, first with acetone–hydrochloric acid–water (50 : 5 : 5) and then with N magnesium chloride solution.

Rapid separation of amino acid mixtures by two-dimensional chromatography on sheets of modified celluloses (Knight, 1959b) and resin-loaded papers (Knight, 1960) can be achieved. Although a good distribution of spots over much of the area of the chromatogram occurs, the individual spots are all rather diffuse. This applies to the separation of complex mixtures of amino acids on cellulose phosphate paper, using 0·02M sodium buffer of pH 4·7 for development in the first direction, during which the ion-exchange mechanism predominated. In the second direction, *m*-cresol–1 per cent ammonia was used to develop the chromatogram. This converted the amino acids to their anionic forms and the separation occurred as on unmodified cellulose. On DEAE cellulose, developed first with 0·02M acetate buffer of pH 7·5 and then with *m*-cresol–1 per cent ammonia, even more diffuse spots were obtained. The overall time taken for these separations was only half that required for conventional paper chromatography.

More sharply defined spots can be obtained using specially prepared paper loaded with Zeo-Karb 225 sulphonated polystyrene ion-exchange resin. Unfortunately suitable paper of this type is not yet available commercially. Such papers are developed first with 0·2M, pH 3·1 buffer and then in the second direction with *m*-cresol–0·3 per cent ammonia with ammonia in the tank. The resulting chromatogram shows a high degree of resolution and a good distribution of spots. The definition of the individual spots can be even further improved by using a wick feed to slow down the rate of solvent movement. Two-dimensional chromatography on resin-loaded papers would appear to be a very promising method for the separation of amino acids, especially as it is comparatively insensitive to variations in experimental conditions and to interference by salt, which, as already emphasized, will cause distortion of spots in conventional paper chromatography. Selection of the grade of resin and the method employed for its incorporation into the paper are of critical importance in chromatography of this kind. Further developments in this field must therefore depend largely on the availability of rigorously standardized resin-loaded papers.

Knight (1960, 1962) has compared the migration of amino acids on ion-exchange cellulose papers, resin-loaded papers and ion-exchange resins. On all three media, under conditions where ion-exchange can operate, the ionic properties are only sufficient broadly to segregate the spots into the three classes, acidic, neutral and basic amino acids. Within each class the relative rates of migration of individual amino acids follow the same order on resin-loaded paper as on a column of resin of the type incorporated in the paper, eluted with the same buffer solution.

Thus, under 'ion-exchange' conditions, the cellulose of the paper acts merely as a hydrophilic support and the increasing affinity of the amino acids for the lipophilic matrix of the dispersed resin particles causes increasing retardation of spot movement in the order glycine, alanine, valine, leucines, for those with aliphatic hydrocarbon side chains. The non-ionic characteristic, side-chain length, determines the lipophilic nature and hence the affinity for the resin matrix. This principle also applies to separation on the modified cellulose papers but the order of migration is in this case reversed. This is to be expected because of the hydrophilic nature of the cellulose matrix which has little affinity for the longer hydrocarbon side chains. Substitution of a hydroxy group in an amino-acid side chain enhances its hydrophilic nature and hence increases the rate of migration on resin-loaded paper but decreases it on modified cellulose.

Thin-layer Chromatography

Chromatography in which a thin layer of an inorganic adsorbent coated on a glass plate is used as the stationary phase, has been attempted by a number of workers for at least 25 years. Interest in the method has recently been stimulated by the work of Stahl (1958), who standardized the adsorbents used and made the procedure more reproducible. The particular attraction of this method is that it combines the simplicity associated with the use of sheets of material, as in paper chromatography, with the possibility of using almost any one of the many inorganic adsorbents (e.g. silica gel, aluminium oxide and kieselguhr) usually employed only in columns. More recently the method has been extended to include cellulose and modified cellulose (e.g. acetylated, phosphorylated, carboxymethyl, DEAE, and ECTEOLA cellulose).

Thin-layer techniques are very rapid, even compared with paper chromatography, typical development times being only 30–60 min. This is useful for the separation of unstable substances. Drying of the plates after development of the chromatogram is also rapid. The thin layer of stationary phase permits a high degree of resolution if small spots are initially applied, as they remain remarkably sharp during development of the chromatogram. For this reason, the sensitivity of the method is high and the lower limits for the detection of substances is usually even less than for paper chromatography. When the adsorbents employed are entirely inorganic, high temperatures and corrosive reagents may be used for revealing the positions of spots. For the detection of unreactive organic substances, it is possible, therefore, to heat with sulphuric acid and so produce charred spots.

Procedure for Preparing and Using Thin-layer Plates. The adsorbent selected should be of a special grade (e.g. Merck), manufactured so as to comply with the specifications suggested by Stahl, for resolution of test mixtures of dyes with specified solvents, and rate of solvent movement. Suitable granularity and ability to adhere to the plate are also important. Sometimes an inert filler is mixed with the adsorbent in order to improve this latter property. The selected adsorbent or mixture is coated on to 20-cm square glass plates, preferably by means of a spreading device (Fig. 7.2) which applies a uniform coat approximately 250 μm in thickness.

It is convenient to coat five plates at the same time, the entire operation of preparing the paste and coating being carried out as quickly as possible because the paste sets in about 4 min. To coat five plates, 30 g of suitable adsorbent are uniformly mixed in a mortar with 60 ml of distilled water. The paste is transferred to the spreader and, with a single steady movement, is smoothly applied to the plates, which are placed in a row and held down to the instrument base by a capillary film of water. The plates are then left exposed to the air until dry, the process being hastened, if necessary, by a current of warm air.

For the chromatography of hydrophobic compounds it is usually advisable to activate the adsorbent by heating the plates for 30 min at 120° C. This is usually unnecessary when the substances to be separated are hydrophilic. Plates are most active immediately after heating and gradually pick up moisture and lose their activity, when exposed to a moist atmosphere; they should therefore be stored in a desiccator until required.

Before applying the substances to be separated, it is useful to mark a starting line 1·5 cm from one edge of the plate and another one parallel to it near the other edge to denote the limit for advance of the solvent front. Spots of the sample solutions (at a concentration of, say, 0·1–1 per cent) are applied at marked points along the starting line by the method used for paper chromatography. These spots should be kept as small as possible, if necessary by applying several small portions consecutively, drying each with a hair dryer before adding the next, until a total of 5–10 μl of solution has been transferred to each small area of the plate. Alternatively, a line of minute

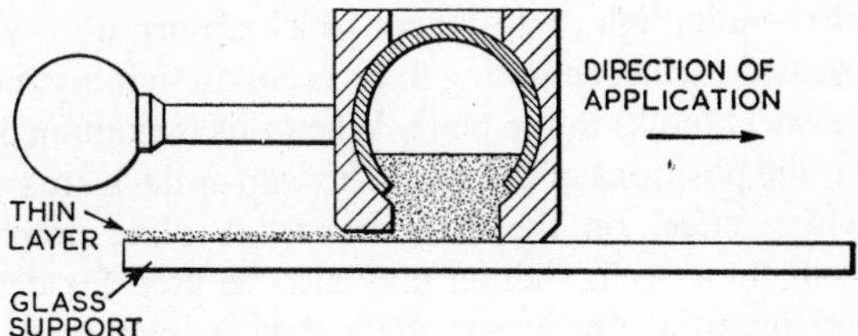

FIG. 7.2. Side view of applicator for production of plates for thin-layer chromatography.

spots may be placed at right angles to the direction of solvent movement.

The chromatograms are developed by ascending chromatography in suitable glass tanks containing a layer of solvent 5–7 mm deep in the bottom of the tank. A number of vertical strips of glass fibre paper, wetted with the solvent, are placed against the larger walls of the tank, in order to saturate the air surrounding the plates with the solvent vapour. This precaution prevents non-uniform R_f values across the width of the plate, due to greater evaporation of solvent from near the edges, and also reduces the time for development. The plates are placed so that their lower edge, near the starting line, rests on the bottom of the tank and so dips into the solvent, and then the lid is quickly fitted. When the solvent reaches the second line drawn on the plate, development is stopped by removing the plates from the tank and allowing them to dry at room temperature.

The positions of the spots are then revealed by any of the methods described for paper chromatography (see page 95). In addition, reagents which would attack paper can be used. When, for instance, 50 per cent sulphuric acid is employed as a general spray for organic substances, it is useful to 'develop' the plate two or three times, restricting the distance of solvent flow a little more after each development before applying the samples to be separated. In this way organic impurities in the adsorbent, which tend to become concentrated in the solvent front, appear in the final chromatogram as a series of black lines of diminishing intensity, and can be readily distinguished from true spots of high R_f value. For spraying reagents on to thin-layer plates, it is essential to use a sprayer which produces a very fine cloud of droplets, as it is easy to damage the surface of the adsorbent if a coarse spray is ejected.

Fluorescent substances may be detected by viewing the chromatogram in ultra-violet light. Substances which absorb ultra-violet light may be revealed by incorporating fluorescein or an inorganic fluorescent substance (Merck) in the plate. When this is examined by ultra-violet light, the positions of the spots show up as dark areas, owing to the quenching effect on the fluorescence. A plate prepared with 0·04 per cent fluorescein sodium may also be used for detection of unsaturated organic substances. After development and drying, a little bromine vapour is blown over the plate which turns red and no longer fluoresces except for the positions occupied by unsaturated substances, which still give a yellowish-green fluorescence.

Records of finished chromatograms may be made by black and white or colour photography before washing off the coating from the glass plates, which are then available for re-use. Alternatively, the actual chromatogram itself may be preserved for future reference by spraying it with an aqueous dispersion of a plastic such as Neatan (Merck), which, when dry, forms a film over the surface of the chromatogram. Pieces of adhesive tape are fixed around the edges of the sheet, which is dipped in water for a short time. The chromatogram is then gently peeled away from the glass, placed on a sheet of filter paper, and allowed to dry in the air. The detached film may be stored, in the dark, for a long time without fading of colours.

A convenient small-scale version of thin-layer chromatography is possible by spreading the adsorbent manually on microscope slides which are then used for the chromatographic separation of single samples. The slides may be developed by the ascending method in a beaker covered by a watch glass.

Chromatography in Layers of Adsorbent on Plates Inclined at a slight Angle

For this chromatographic method a layer of the dry adsorbent is spread over a sheet of glass, which is then maintained at an angle of about 15° from the horizontal. A suitably even layer of adsorbent, divided lengthwise into strips, can be obtained easily by rolling out a sufficient quantity of the powder with a thick rod on which are several rings cut from rubber tube (Fig. 7.3). To minimize evaporation, the glass plate with the adsorbent already spread out is placed in a closed chamber. Solvent is then fed into the lower end of the strips

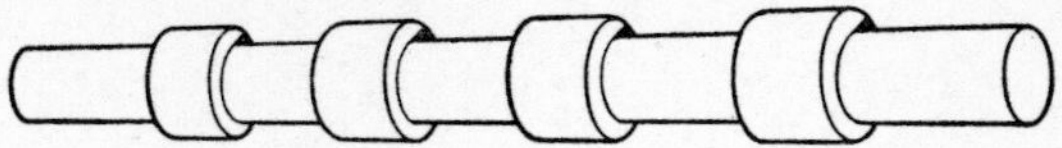

FIG. 7.3. Rod for spreading dry adsorbent on glass plates.

of adsorbent. The mixtures of substances to be separated are then added to the strips near to their lower ends. When separation is sufficiently far advanced, development of colours to reveal the band positions can be done, either by spraying as for thin-layer plates, or by applying the revealing solution by means of a pipette along the edge of each strip, which is allowed to soak into the adsorbent. The advantage of this form of chromatography is that the layer can be of any thickness up to approximately 1 cm, and greater amounts of material can be separated than in the thin-layer technique. Recovery of the separated substances is particularly easy because the column of adsorbent does not require preliminary extrusion from the tube, as it does in the conventional chromatogram.

REFERENCES

Bendich, A., Fresco, J. R., Rosenkranz, H. S. and Beiser, S. M. (1955). *J. Amer. chem. Soc.* **77**, 3671.

Flodin, P. (1962). *Dextran Gels and their Application in Gel Filtration.* Pharmacia, Uppsala.

Head, A. J., Kember, N. F., Miller, R. P. and Wells, R. A. (1958). *J. chem. Soc.* 34.

Knight, C. S. (1959a). *Nature, Lond.* **183**, 165.

Knight, C. S. (1959b). *Nature, Lond.* **184,** 1486.

Knight, C. S. (1960). *Nature, Lond.* **188,** 739.

Knight, C. S. (1962). *J. Chromatog.* **8,** 205.
Peterson, E. A. and Sober, H. A. (1956). *J. Amer. chem. Soc.* **78,** 751.
Porath, J. (1957). *Arkiv Kemi Mineral. Geol.* **11,** 97.
Porath, J. and Flodin, P. (1959). *Nature, Lond.* **183,** 1657.
Sober, H. A. and Peterson, E. A. (1958). *Federation Proc.* **17,** 1116.
Sober, H. A. and Peterson, E. A. (1960). *Amino Acids, Proteins and Cancer Biochemistry*, 61. Academic Press, N.Y.
Staehelin, M., Peterson, E. A. and Sober, H. A. (1959). *Arch. Biochem. Biophys.* **85,** 289.
Stahl, E. (1958). *Mitteilung* 11, *Chemiker-Zeitung* **82,** 323.
Stewart, J. W. and Stahmann, M. A. (1962). *J. Chromatog.* **9,** 233.

INDEX